Rachel
20100
Boca Raton, FL 33434-5238

MW00606237

PH: 561 405 6480
cell: 917 8335380
e-mail: Irpatron @ AOL.com

Sun-flower in the snow

Tales from a wartime childhood by

Rachel Patron

trimarkpress

LIBRARY OF CONGRESS CATALOGING-IN-PUBLICATION DATA

SUNFLOWER IN THE SNOW
BY RACHEL PATRON

P.   CM.

ISBN: 978-1-943401-68-0
LIBRARY OF CONGRESS CONTROL NUMBER: 2019920681

A-20

FIRST EDITION
PRINTED AND BOUND IN THE UNITED STATES OF AMERICA

A PUBLICATION OF TRIMARK PRESS, INC

368 SOUTH MILITARY TRAIL
DEERFIELD BEACH, FL 33442
800.889.0693
WWW.TRIMARKPRESS.COMTA

In Memory of my Mother,
Esther Rakowski Rubinow.

At dawn, whole fields of sunflowers stand at attention,

All facing east, and begin their romance with the rising sun.

Young flowers follow its light through the day,

Looking up, then over and westward,

Catching one final glance as the sun disappears over the horizon.

Joanna Klein
New York Science Times

PROLOGUE

Much happened before I was born on January 3, 1936 in our ancestral city of Bialystok, Poland. Americans may not be able to find my birthplace on a map, but they often hear surnames such as: Bialystok, Bialostokker, Bialostocki and other derivatives of the city where I had spent the first five years of my life. Why such a proliferation of names? Because so many Bialystok Jews had come to the United States.

Unfortunately, not enough.

Bialystok is located in northeastern Poland, 40 kilometers west of Belarus and the vastness of Imperial Russia, and later the Soviet Union. Another important fact: Untill World War II, Bialystok was the only city in Europe with a majority Jewish population. Of its 100 thousand inhabitants, 60% were Jews.

How did this happen, and why was the Jewish population in Poland larger than in any European country? The origin is an ancient love story, an affair between Polish King Casimir, the only one called "The Great," and a raven-haired Jewess named Esterka. (Jewish mistresses of noble Christians are usually described as "raven-haired!") This liason lasted from 1334, when Casimir ascended the throne, till his death in 1370.

Esterka convinced His Majesty to issue a decree proclaiming Polish Jews as "protected people of the King," and anyone harming them would be severely punished. She also prevailed upon her royal lover to urge Jewish settlement in Poland. The timing could not have been better since hundreds of Jewish communities had been devastated by the massacres of the Crusades, casting their inhabitants adrift and in search of safe harbor.

This is how my ancestors, the Rakowskis and the Rubinows, ended up in Poland, and eventually settled in Bialystok. And there they stayed for over five-hundred years.

I would be rebuked by my dead ancestors if I failed to mention how smart my mother's family was. The Rakowskis were rightfully famous for their learning, the scholarly books they wrote, the Talmudic tractates they interpreted, and the sublime oratory they thundered from their rabbinic pulpits. Thirty-Six uninterrupted generations of rabbis! How many families can make such a claim? As the last Rakowski, I inherited a document tracing us directly to Rashi, the greatest Jewish scholar of 11th century France. A solid, unassailable document, my mother assured us.

Of my father's family, the Rubinows, suffice it to say here that they were rich. More details to follow.

So where to begin my story? The best starting point is the dawn of the 20th century, before World War I, the first convulsion of modern times. 1913 is about right, a time when Europe was still aglow with peace, (more or less), and Czar Nicholas II ruled both Poland and Russia.

And lastly: My mother's name was Esterka.

PART ONE:
THREE COWS DRINKING
WATER

CHAPTER ONE

My grandfather, Rabbi Jacob Meyer Rakowski, was restless.

Every morning after prayers, he sprinted out of his synagogue, Mishkan Elohim, to take a brisk walk along Bialystok's broadest avenue, Zwirki Wigury. Here the brick houses were luxurious, surrounded by trees and flowerbeds. Christians lived here, while the multitude of the city's Jews lived on the "other" side, known as the Jewish Quarter. To exhibit his contrarian nature, the Rabbi walked among the gentiles, clad in his long black garment, a black velvet yarmulke atop his head. He was short, but handsome, with piercing black eyes, capable of changing from anger to joy in a second.

Jews who noticed his purposeful stride told each other admiringly, "The Rabbi is deep in thought about the Almighty's relentless task of shielding His Chosen People from harm."

Untrue! God was not on my grandfather's mind as he vigorously marched back to the Jewish Quarter, a place of modest two-story wooden houses nestled along narrow streets, his own home, blessedly, just two blocks from the synagogue.

Since I mention broad avenues and narrow streets, you might wonder: Just how big is Bialystok? Well, when I was three years old and my parents took me to a restaurant, I sat on our city's telephone directory—and was able to reach the table. Our big city was also the capital of Podlasie County in Eastern Poland.

On this particular morning, Grandfather burst through the door, shouting, "Elena, children, come here! I have wonderful news!"

His wife came in from the kitchen, licking the wooden spoon from the pancake batter she had been mixing. With fine cheekbones and prematurely greying hair, she was too thin for a mother of six. She explained her weight by pointing out that she had little time to sit down for a proper meal when her husband was noisily pacing the wooden planks, as if trying to break through the ceiling into the arms of God.

Grandfather sat at the kitchen table and addressed his wife, four daughters, and one son still living at home.

"I have decided that we must become farmers."

Silence. His wife and children stared at him with concern. Elena coughed, as if choking on her spoon.

"Nu?" Jacob Meyer prompted.

Grandmother recovered somewhat. "Yakov, your people have been rabbis for centuries, and not even one ran away from his duties to become a farmer."

Her son, Lev, chuckled. He had just graduated from high school at seventeen, enrolled in a professional engineering school, and devoted his free time to ogling girls. Of Elena's daughters, Fanya was the oldest, now fifteen, born in 1892. Serious and smart, she combed her hair into a thick black braid tied with a

4

black ribbon. Next was Esther, nicknamed Fira, thirteen, who resembled a romantic heroine, complete with blond locks and dreamy eyes. (My future mother!) Zila, eleven, was a spitfire, like her father. She wiggled her hips while walking and was rewarded with appreciative whistles from neighborhood boys.

The youngest, Mina, was nine.

"She was my last latke," Grandmother would say. "You know, when you prepare a potato mix to make pancakes. First come the perfectly round ones, but for the last one you scrape the bottom and sides and what comes out is smaller and uneven."

Mina was smart enough to attach herself to her sister Zila and follow her around wherever she could. Good-natured Zila accepted that it was her duty to take care of her little sister.

Grandfather spread his hands on the table, palms down, and announced, "I bought a farm in Sokolka."

The announcement rendered his family shell-shocked. When they finally understood that it was not a joke, their faces revealed a deep sense of gloom.

Grandfather tried again. "It is time for Jews to live as our ancestors had in ancient Israel."

"Papa, do you think you're King David?" Fanya asked sardonically.

His wife was more to the point. "With what money shall we become farmers?"

"Good question. As you all know, for the past four years I have been supplying schmaltz herring to the Russian Cavalry unit stationed on the outskirts of town. Oy, how the Czar's horsemen love Jewish herring! And with the herring money I bought us a small farm."

Elena wiped her forehead with her batter-stained apron. "I said all along that God should have never allowed you to undertake the undignified herring trade."

"Papa, how can we leave Marek alone?" Fanya asked. Marek, Grandfather's oldest child, was serving a sentence in the local Czarist jail for organizing a socialist protest march.

"Fanichka, your brother Marek is never alone. He has a whole bunch of other prisoners who listen to his sermons on the need for a Marxist revolution."

"Will you force us to milk cows?" Esther asked, inspecting her beautiful hands.

"I have money only for a horse. And you cannot milk a horse."

Zila sulked. "We'll have no friends there! Jews don't farm. Papa, God will not be happy watching you abandon Torah for a horse."

As always, Mina remained silent.

It was a slow ride to Sokolka, which was only fourteen kilometers from Bialystok. They hitched the horse—their future farm animal—to a buggy laden with household goods and clothes. Six of them undertook the journey, Lev remaining in the city to continue his studies, guard the house, and visit Marek in jail at least once a week.

"Let's go, Amos!" Grandfather called out to the horse. He had named him after a prophet who had the wisdom to write only nine chapters. Brief and meaningful.

It was summertime, and the country they passed was lush with greenery. Fragrant air filled their lungs, a far cry from the city dust of the Jewish Quarter, in which many of the streets were unpaved. The countryside they were now in was home to sanatoriums for people with consumption. The air alone was enough to heal them, said the mavens of maladies.

The Rakowskis entered the village of Sokolka in late afternoon, to the astonished eyes of local farmers. These were hard men with hard faces, and they were not fond of strangers. The family spent the rest of the day and half the night getting settled. Exhausted, they finally fell asleep. Only Grandfather woke up early the next morning, put on his black garment and velvet yarmulke and hitched a sleepy Amos to the second-hand plough he had bought in Bialystok on the farmers' market day. This done, the freshly minted farmer grabbed the reins and whistled as he had seen the Polish farmers do. As he began to plough his land, he chanted his morning prayers.

Alas, the prayers went unanswered. Amos appeared to be dozing while standing on all four, disregarding his owner's impatient orders. The locals roared with laughter; Grandfather was unsure if their disrespect was meant for Amos or him.

The same scene was repeated each morning. Even a well-rested Amos refused to work, as if in cahoots with the sneering farmers. To make himself more farmer-like, Grandfather visited the Sokolka store, where he bought a peasant shirt and, in the back room, an overpriced rifle. That will teach them! He thought. He was right: the firearm displayed on top of the plough stopped the farmers' jeering, but failed to convince Amos to perform the duties for which he had been purchased.

Elena and the girls planted a garden, which did not grow anything they could eat. Food was expensive, and Grandfather suspected the farmers of overcharging.

In 1914, the Great War rescued them from farming. Grandfather sold the plough for half the price he had paid for it. A happy Rakowski family hitched Amos to the buggy, and at a faster pace than before, headed back to Bialystok. There, Grandfather resumed his pulpit duties, appreciating the cries of joy from his congregation. Having squandered his savings on a dream, he needed extra income. Back he went to the garrison with a pail of schmaltz herring.

Unfortunately, the Czar's Cavalry, now on its last hooves, was in no need of herring. And in 1916, when the Great War was over, Poland became an independent Republic.

My father, Jacob Rubinow, was gorgeous. After hearing this for years from adoring aunts and other female visitors, he adjusted to his burden. Yes, I am gorgeous, he told himself. He had little sense of humor, but a lot of confidence. At age sixteen, he was already six-feet-two, at a time when Christians believed that Jews were midgets. And one more thing, this handsome boy was also rich.

So, what could be wrong in young Jacob's life? His father! Mark Rubinow was a rich textile manufacturer, textiles being the mainstay of Bialystok's economy. It was commonly agreed that my grandfather Mark, was mean. Some argued that he was the meanest man in town, although this opinion was hard to prove. He was tall, six-foot-one, and might have been considered handsome had it not been for his perpetual scowl.

What bothered Mark Rubinow most was the age difference between him and his beautiful wife. Twenty-one years! Jadwiga Shmukler—in Hebrew Yoheved—was also Mark's second cousin. Proof of the bloodline was Jadwiga's stunning height of five-feet-eight. When my father turned sixteen, his mother was forty-five and his father sixty-six. Mark had no one to blame but himself for the age difference. As a bachelor pushing forty, he had rejected every girl presented to him: too short, too ugly, too stupid. But when his cousin Jadwiga showed up—boom! Love at first sight. At least on Mark's part. He was too smitten to reflect why the beautiful, but impoverished, Jadwiga would desire to marry a rich old man.

By 1917, the Rubinows were parents to three children. My father Jacob, nicknamed Kuba, was the middle child, born in 1900. An older brother, Joseph, nicknamed Ossya, was nineteen and a student in the Commerce Department of Bialystok University. The youngest, fourteen-year-old Sonya, no nickname, who exhibited an enormous musical talent, had for the past six years relentlessly studied violin.

Old Man Rubinow hung a whip over the fireplace in their luxurious mansion on the outskirts of town. The whip had never touched Ossya's or Sonya's buttocks, but was strictly reserved for Kuba. A psychiatrist might have concluded that the reason for the fatherly corporal punishment was his wife's demonstrative love for her middle son, whose devotion to her was just as fierce. Mark's suspicion, later proven correct, was that Jadwiga loved her son more than she loved him.

Kuba tried as best he could to stay out of his father's sight. But on one particular spring day, coming home from his last year at the gymnasium, he intended to sneak into the house through the back door and tiptoe upstairs to his room.

It was not to be. His father was lurking in the back hall, whip in hand, eyes aglow.

"You detritus of the human race!" He screamed. "You think you can disrespect your father and sneak into my house without a proper greeting?"

Father circled around Mark, then ran into the vast salon in search of his mother. Alas, no Jadwiga. Oh, how Kuba was tired of his father's never-ending rage! He was still hurting from the last beating a few days earlier. When Mark reached the salon, hand gripping the torture instrument, my father rushed out of the house and took off down the road.

Young and fit, he ran as fast as his legs would carry him, emboldened by a fresh resolve to never again become the victim of another thrashing. After a while he paused, and looked back. To his amazement, Mark was still in hot pursuit, firmly clutching the whip.

Onward ran the young rascal, his body energized by his anger. His calves hurt and his heart pounded, but his legs sprinted along. He breathed hard, then again looked back. What the hell! His father was still chugging away, now a weary silhouette. His anger undiminished, he took off again, uttering every Russian curse he knew, which took a while, because Russian is a language endowed with many curses.

The next time he stopped and looked back, the road was clear. My father sat down and reflected. This would be his first independent decision. Returning home he would be subjected to unbelievable bodily harm. There was simply no way for him but to continue. He got up, dusted himself off, and proceeded on foot toward the Russian border. Minsk, the capital of Belarus, was only forty kilometers away.

Before my father unfolded the vastness of Russia in the year 1917. Pampered and inexperienced, he nonetheless had certain qualities in his favor. He spoke fluent Russian, was tall, swarthy and, as I've mentioned, gorgeous. He knew he must present himself as a Christian, an Armenian perhaps, say: Yakov Rubinian.

At the first farm he came to, Kuba offered his labor for food and lodgings. After a week, he told his employer that he must move on. Could they spare a shirt and a jacket? Yes, dear boy. And a few rubles for the road? Yes, you are such a good worker.

At this point in its history, Russia was filled with vagabonds, as if the entire population was on the move, migrating from one peril to the next, perhaps believing that the earth was shattering under their feet, and the only way to save themselves was to keep moving. Unlike these Russians, Father was not a fatalist, but a realist. To him it was possible, even likely, that one place might be better than the last. During his wanderings, he subsisted on the generosity of Russian peasants, with whose fate he was somehow able to identify. He melted into the throngs of army deserters, persecuted bureaucrats, and displaced nobles pretending to be peasants, many of whom met far less success than Father.

For the first time in his life, he was free. And for the first time in his life, he was poor.

Somehow, this self-styled young Armenian found himself in Saint Petersburg on a day when a Russian mob, led by a Communist called Vladimir Lenin, broke into the Czar's Winter Palace and hoisted a red flag on it. The disturbance lasted no more than an hour, and the happy mob dispersed to celebrate its victory with vodka and sour pickles.

There was no work for Father in the big city, so he moved on. After talking to some folks in a tavern, he decided to make his way to Odessa, a warm water port with a reputation for generosity and good humor, not traits often encountered in this land of woe.

Once in Odessa, he rented a room and enrolled in the famous Odessa Polytechnical University. No one asked for his high school diploma, a good thing, because he had none. What they were looking for were mathematicians, a field in which Father excelled. The only downside was the strange curriculum of only one subject: Marxist Economics. But what the hell? The studies were free and so was the food.

For the next three years, Father studied a little and enjoyed himself a lot since Odessa had been spared the famine and dislocations of the Revolutionary Wars. Then, in 1920, an encounter challenged Father's tranquility. It was announced on campus that the new Soviet leader, Joseph Stalin, would appear that night in the Student Assembly Hall to address the young Communist intellectuals. As the man with the dark hair and bushy mustache, dressed in a belted khaki shirt, strode onto the podium, Father thought: I am much taller than he.

It was his last happy thought.

Like many speakers of the era, Stalin droned on and on about the virtues of Communism, freedom and equality for the proletariat, free this, free that, and so on. It was a sermon so common that my father barely listened. Then, all of a sudden, Stalin raised his voice. Father sat up straight.

"If I ever betray the Revolution," Stalin pointed a finger at the audience. "If I ever betray the Revolution, let the executioner cut off my head, and let this head of mine roll down my beloved Moscow boulevards, blood gushing out of it to fertilize the soil of the Revolution and Mother Russia…"

For a moment, the audience was stunned. Then everyone stood and applauded, as did my father. But his mind telegraphed: this man is a lunatic. Would a normal person imagine such sadistic garbage about himself?

As applause echoed through the hall, Father slipped away unnoticed, returned to his lodgings, packed his rucksack, and disappeared once more into the tumult of the emerging Soviet Union.

CHAPTER TWO

My grandparents, Elena and Jacob Meyer, were worried. Their four daughters were not only unmarried, but not even spoken for. Moreover, their oldest, Fanya, was already twenty-five, and her sister Esther, twenty-one, a four-year difference that made finding a groom for Fanya an emergency.

Still, Jacob and Elena were realistic enough to acknowledge the reasons behind their unhappy situation. Although the Rakowskis were an illustrious family of rabbis and scholars going back to the eleventh century, the current generation was not living up to its past glory. The rabbi's two sons were not interested in Jewish scholarship. Worse, they were not pious, preferring to wander around in pursuit of foreign learning. The oldest, Marek, who should have been a rabbi, was released from prison and stayed a while with his family in Bialystok. Shortly thereafter he moved to Warsaw, where he became a socialist writer and editor of his own magazine, The Jewish Worker. In every issue, he included his own humorous story, more often than not too rowdy for religious people to read. The one still at home was Lev, a nice young man more interested in building things than in studying Torah. It was also rumored, though good-naturedly, that Lev courted only rich girls.

Compared to their brothers, the Rakowski girls were without blemish. Maybe Fanya, now considered old, was too smart for her own good. Esther was pretty, yes, but her manner revealed that the last thing she was interested in was cooking and cleaning house. Zila was deemed too social, a butterfly searching for a good time, not a righteous marriage. Mina was too young to marry, so the gossipy yentes left her alone.

All this might have been acceptable to potential suitors if the girls had decent dowries. But alas, the Rakowskis were poor.

Jacob Meyer and Elena avoided the conversation about their daughters' future for as long as they could, which was not very long. Then one afternoon, when they were alone, Elena said ominously to her husband, "We must talk."

The Rabbi grunted, fearing the worst. His wife put in front of him a slice of his favorite babka. After a minute or two, she said, "I have been in touch with Puah." Jacob stopped chewing. "She and I agree that the girls must learn a skill, so if worse comes to worse…"

"No!" Grandfather hit the oilcloth with his fist. "Our girls are the most beautiful and virtuous of all brides in Bialystok. Any boy who marries them should thank God a million times."

"Yes." Elena sighed. "But in the meantime, Puah suggests that we send them to her in Warsaw so they can learn a trade."

"So, you will let my Bolshevik sister teach our daughters how to live their lives?"

"Puah is a normal socialist, and also a famous Zionist. She

knows everyone in Warsaw and will do anything for her beloved nieces."

The girls were excited at the prospect of traveling to Warsaw and staying with their famous atheist aunt. On the train, they recalled Puah's legendary past. She was the oldest of the dozen children born to Rabbi Menahem Mendel Rakowski and his wife, Rachel, after whom I am named. Puah claimed to be the smartest of the bunch, certainly smarter than her brother Jacob Meyer. At age fifteen, she was married off to a man two decades her senior, an itinerant cantor by trade. Her hair was shorn and covered with a wig. By age twenty-one, she had borne three children. Her marriage and early childbearing convinced her of God's alienation from mankind. Since her husband was often away, she began plotting her escape to Warsaw.

Puah's first rebellious act was to grow out her hair under the wig. "It itched like hell," she would later recount. Other than her own hair, an escaping woman needs cash. So, she began putting aside money from her household allowance. Miraculously, her mother Rachel and father, Rabbi Menahem Mendel, agreed that her husband was an uncaring scoundrel, and promised to help. They found a small apartment for her and their grandchildren in Warsaw. According to family legend, on her way to the train station, Puah tossed her wig into the gutter.

In Warsaw, Puah hired someone to look after her children and threw herself into an accelerated course to finish high school in one year. She also enrolled in a teachers' college. Soon, a high school diploma and a teaching certificate were her reward.

Eventually, Puah met every Jewish rebel and dreamer in Poland's capital. And one day, with the help of her lover whom she called "Comrade Birnbaum," she opened the first secular Jewish girls' school in Eastern Europe, and became the first female Jewish teacher.

This aunt, who was now greeting them at the door, was beautiful, but serious. They would later report to their parents that socialism is a serious occupation.

During a dinner of mystery stew with Puah and Comrade Birnbaum, their aunt said, "Girls, I have enrolled you in brasserie-making school."

The girls' spoons fell back into their bowls. Only Comrade Birnbaum continued eating heartily.

Fanya hung her head. "I would prefer to study medicine."

Puah smiled compassionately. "Yes, Fanichka. But we don't live in Dreamland. In the real world women will always need brasseries."

"I know nothing about sewing," my mother said mournfully.

Puah's response was clipped. "They'll teach you."

Unexpectedly, Zila was elated. "I like sewing!" Mina, clutching her sister's hand, said nothing.

The girls spent five hours each day in a musty loft on Nalewki Street, where they made drawings of brasseries, then stitched them in white cotton on a dummy, while all the time trying to become proficient in coordinating their hands and feet to operate a sewing machine.

The class numbered ten women, not all of them Jewish. After a month of learning, they were divided into couples, and assigned to sew brasseries for each other. Fanya's and Esther's creations were adequate. Zila's were gorgeous and unique. How was she able to transform the cheap cotton into a dainty frou-frou worthy of an elegant lady's boudoir? Everyone applauded, and the instructress predicted, "Zila will go far."

Mina, however, burst into tears. The poor child had sewn a brasserie with only one cup. Zila hugged her despondent sister. "You'll be my assistant, and I'll tell you exactly what to do."

Puah's social life was unusual. Every evening teachers, artists and writers assembled in her "salon<" people whose occupations Grandfather described as "Luft Gesheften," meaning in Yiddish "air business." The rule here was: you ate what you brought. Most sought-after was sausage, black bread and cheap red wine. They sang passionate hymns in Russian and Yiddish about throwing away the shackles of bondage and rebuilding the ancient land of Zion.

But the most intense activity was staring out of the window toward the massive building across the street, an impenetrable edifice of stone and brick surrounded by barbed wire. It was the Warsaw prison for "enemies of the state," in which many of the husbands or wives of the assembled were serving sentences for "agitation." Each evening before dusk, a throng of prisoners would appear on the roof. Puah's guests were already lined up, hollering at the top of their voices, to which the prisoners responded boisterously.

Theirs was a cozy revolution.

My grandmother, Jadwiga Rubinow, was boarding a train to Paris. She was alone, because my grandfather Mark had no place in her life any longer. The Great War had rendered them poor. Actually, Jadwiga hated the word "poor," especially when applied to herself. She preferred: "temporarily insolvent." They no longer owned the big house on the outskirts of Bialystok. Also gone was the whip, its burial place unknown. With whatever savings she could salvage, Grandmother rented a three-bedroom apartment in an "almost-elegant" part of town, confining her husband to the smallest room. The extra bedroom was reserved for her beloved son, Kuba, when he returned, as Jadwiga was sure he would.

It was late afternoon on Avenue Foch in Paris, with autumn leaves falling on the boulevard. Jadwiga stood in front of a window display of her favorite designer, Elsa Schiaparelli. She wore a five-year old Schiaparelli ensemble, a purchase she had made in 1916 when she and Mark visited here for the last time as rich folk. At the time, Mark had bought for himself an exorbitantly priced camel hair coat.

The old design looked good on Jadwiga. She could carry off a garment better than anyone in Bialystok, where she was famous for her unique sense of style. It was not only her height and regal bearing, but also the air of confidence she bestowed on any garment that touched her skin.

She checked the new styles in the window. They were looser than before the war, not meant to be worn with a corset. She had never seen a dropped waistline, untailored and without cinches or darts. Since she could not afford to buy the dress, she would sketch it. Maybe a clever seamstress in Bialystok could fashion one from her drawing. When she finished, she was pleased with the result, a perfect rendering of a modern silhouette.

The next day, Jadwiga returned to the avenue with a good quality sketchpad and charcoals. The result was a detailed sketch of a tweed costume from the window. She substituted a green velvet skirt instead of brown tweed and added a romantic lace blouse. Magnifique!

Day three was devoted to Chanel, the simplest and most amazing sorceress of couture. To wear Chanel, you must be brave or rich enough to dare prejudice. For a week, Grandmother sketched obsessively. I cannot possibly wear all these fashions, she admitted to herself. As her train was speeding back to Bialystok, she had a brilliant idea: She would open the Bialystok Salon of Haute Couture/Original Designs by Madame Jadwiga. Bialystok, a city of 100,000 inhabitants with its own magnificent Ritz Hotel, did not possess even one elegant dress shop. Rich Bialystok matrons traveled to Warsaw and paid outrageous prices for atrocious gowns. Jadwiga would have a built-in clientele of friends and admirers eager to spread the news about the elegance coming to their city.

Grandmother took the sketches to Agnieszka, a seamstress who had done work for her in the good old days. Agnieszka was impressed. "These sketches are wonderful."

There was no better environment for sewing than Bialystok. Even after the wartime losses, the city remained home to two hundred-twenty textile factories, most of them owned by Jews. Soon Jadwiga's first copied design came to life, then two more. She contacted merchants with whom her husband had done business, as well as people she had met socially. She invited them to the back room of her favorite restaurant, Count Potocki. There she modeled five different outfits. The audience applauded enthusiastically.

Jadwiga laid out her ambitious scheme to open her fashion salon. She always concluded her pitch with, "I need you to invest in me, and I guarantee you will not be sorry. I shall make certain that every woman who shops here will look more beautiful in a Jadwiga original than in any gown she could buy in Warsaw or Paris."

Within a month, Grandmother was fully funded. A spacious storefront was rented in the best part of town, on Rynek Kosciuszki Square, under the city clock. She hired four more seamstresses and put Agnieszka in charge. Every imaginable fabric was available. She decorated her shop with Parisian chic and let loose the sewing machines. As the business prospered, she visited Paris at least once a month, returning with new sketches. To every design she appropriated, she added something unique to her personality: a flower in an unexpected spot, a bit of chiffon, a leopard belt.

The women poured in, and the enterprise thrived. Soon gowns in the Grand Opera in Warsaw boasted the Madame Jadwiga label.

In early winter of 1921, as the first snow covered the land, Kuba Rubinow returned home, no longer a lad of sixteen, but a grown man. He and Mark exchanged a cold greeting, after which Father avoided his former tormentor. For the first two weeks, he and Grandmother were inseparable. He visited the shop several times, to the delight of clients and staff. Ah, it's great to be back home, Father thought, I swear to never see Comrade Stalin again.

Well rested and reacclimated, he started looking for a job. It went badly. Everyone knew of him, the Rubinow name famous again not because of Grandfather Mark's wealth, but his mother's business success. The problem was that in newly independent capitalist Poland, no one needed an expert in Marxist Economics.

Then, a breakthrough. Father was hired as a mathematics

teacher in a local high school, having sagely concealed his Marxist degree and presenting himself as a dedicated mathematician and educator. To his discomfort, he soon found himself facing a class of fourteen-year-old boys.

He met his challenge with youthful vigor. Patiently, he explained fractions, simple and compound problems, square roots and geometry. His presentation was crisp and lucid. He was certain that everyone understood. How could they not? But the results of the first test proved Father wrong. About two-thirds of the class failed.

Returning the students' exams, most with inferior grades, Father proclaimed, "I am disappointed in you. Everyone knows that mathematics is the easiest and most beautiful discipline in science."

The youngsters reported to their parents that teacher Rubinow was personally offended by their ignorance. The principal insisted that Father start over. Reluctantly, he complied. The students' grades barely improved. Father suspected that the students pretended not to understand to get back at him, because it was impossible even for fourteen-year-old boys to be so dumb. When the principal insisted on a third tutorial, teacher Rubinow refused, and was summarily fired.

At Friday night dinner, Kuba was seriously depressed. Also, at the table were his brother Ossya with his new wife Mira Los, proudly enhancing her Gypsy-like beauty with large gold earrings and eyes etched with black kohl. No matter that Grandmother Jadwiga believed that her daughter-in-law looked vulgar. What's more, it was the first time that Kuba set eyes on his sister Sonya's fiancé, Miron Hirshhorn, a myopic linguistics teacher visibly awkward in Jadwiga's presence.

Sonya would never forget what her mother had said when first setting eyes on Miron. "This one will be difficult to divorce."

"When the school year ends Miron and I will get married and move to Berlin," Sonya announced. Grandmother raised her eyebrows in displeasure, but Sonya, undaunted, continued, "Miron is so good with languages that he was accepted as a translator in the German Foreign Office. And I shall move heaven and earth to attend the Berlin Philharmonic's apprentice program."

Grandfather Mark ate fast, then excused himself. The others drank sherry and listened to "Swan Lake" on the radio.

Kuba moped around the apartment, unshaven and enveloped in cigarette smoke. Jadwiga felt it was her responsibility to find him a job. But first was an already booked trip to Paris. By now she had become a familiar face in the City of Lights, dining at Maxim's and being photographed in the best nightclubs, surrounded by fashion icons and art celebrities.

A gentleman friend accompanied her to a new club, Chez Czarina, owned by a White Russian who claimed to be related to the Romanovs, a pedigree appropriated by most White Russian nobility in Paris. Here, two handsome young men came over to greet her. They were blond and of the same height, clearly twins, though not identical.

"Madame Jadwiga Rubinow! What a pleasure," said one, as he bent to kiss her hand. "Remember us? Wladyslaw and Kazimierz Wola-Krzysztoporska."

"Yes, I do." She was clearly delighted. "How are you? Oh, I am so sorry about your dear father's passing."

Their father, Count Felix Wola-Krzysztoporska, had passed away in Bialystok a few weeks earlier. The Jews knew Count Felix well since he was one of the few gentile owners of a major textile mill, in this case a factory dyeing fabrics.

Jadwiga invited the twins to join her and her friend. "Do you mind if I call you Wola One and Wola Two? I'm too tipsy to pronounce long names."

The brothers were extremely tipsy as well, which made them eager to pour out their hearts to my grandmother. She gathered that for the past decade they had lived in Paris, leading a life of happy debauchery on a generous allowance from their father. Now, to their chagrin, they had been ordered by the executor of their father's estate to return home and operate the business.

"We know nothing about business," moaned Wola One or Two. "We are boulevardiers. Father had a talent for doing business with all the clever Jews. They would eat us alive."

Which was exactly what Grandmother had in mind.

"I have the perfect solution for you," she said blithely. "My son Jacob is a brilliant businessman with a degree from the Sorbonne. He will be your salvation; I give you my word of honor. He will run the Wola factory and send yo the same amount—or more—as your beloved father."

More hand kissing. Grateful, the brothers drank with my grandmother and her friend well into the night.

Back in Bialystok, Jadwiga handed her untested son a huge and profitable business. This might have been one of the few times in her life that she prayed to God. But she need not have worried. Father turned out to be a great industrial manager. He made sure that every order was delivered on time, even when the destination was abroad. After a while, the Wola factory was thriving, and the playboy brothers in Paris lived extravagantly on the huge allowance sent to them by my father.

Jadwiga's next project was to find Kuba a wife.

CHAPTER THREE

After a year in Warsaw, the four Rakowski brassiere experts returned home. They were congratulated by their parents and brother Lev for having become "professional" ladies. Happily, they consumed Grandmother Elena's sumptuous Sabbath meal and heard Grandfather's erstwhile pronouncement, "If I live till a hundred and twenty, I shall never taste better chicken soup in my life."

"Nu?" Elena asked her daughters.

Fanya went first. "Breasts do not excite me." Lev coughed, spilling soup into his lap. "Anyway, since I can't be a doctor, I would like to study bookkeeping. If you loan me some money, I swear…"

"Don't swear," rebuked her father.

"I promise I'll find a job and pay you back."

"We'll get you the money," Elena assured her.

Zila looked pleased with herself. "I have already made some inquiries and found a job at the Paris Lingerie Salon. I showed them a sample of my stitching, and they liked it." Mina plucked at

Zila's elbow. "Oh yes, and Minochka, too. The owner hired her as my assistant." My little aunt beamed.

Now, everyone's eyes were on Esther. She grinned like a cat hiding a saucer of sour cream.   "My news is the best. I shall be a seamstress at Madame Jadwiga's Haute Couture."

Esther was in awe of Madame Jadwiga. She was unlike any woman my mother had ever met. Aunt Puah came close, but she lived in a world of chaos, whereas Madame was order personified. The showroom's windows shimmered with white lace curtains, pink faille wallpaper and maroon velvet chairs. A bouquet of yellow roses sat on an oblong table next to a tea service of pale green china.

The seamstresses worked in a comfortable back room, equipped with sewing machines, a drafting table, and four mannequins waiting to be draped with fabrics of every color and texture. Jadwiga introduced Mother to them as Miss Esterka Rakowska. To her employer's delight, Esther curtsied. Mother was surprised that only two of the workers were Jewish. Not that it mattered, since she was fluent in Polish.

Mother was truthful with her employer. "I just finished a course in brasserie-making in Warsaw." She showed her the graduation certificate: Solid fives—top marks.

"Brassiere-making!" Jadwiga seemed excited. "That means that you have mastered the art of corsetry." Mother acknowledged that she was able to stitch a corset with whalebones.

For the next week, Grandmother deliberately watched Esther's performance, and, although it lacked daring, it was accurate and dependable. Anyway, good or bad was beside the point. Jadwiga had something else in mind for Esther.

Grandmother made discreet inquiries about the Rakowski family. The Rabbi was a hard man, as were all religious Jews, having spent too much time studying Talmud. She admired the story of the Rabbi's dragging his family into the countryside to become farmers. The man had imagination! Though Jadwiga did not read the Yiddish newspaper, she was aware that the Rabbi's oldest son, Marek, was an excellent, and often hilarious writer, who as a teenager had spent two years in the Czar's jail. And what was deliciously ironic—this son was an atheist!

"I want to make our new employee happy," Jadwiga told Danusia, an excellent seamstress, "so let's gift her a new dress."

On the following Sabbath, Grandmother presented Esther with a pale blue cotton dress, covered with white dots and a ruffle at the hem. With her ash blond curls and dreamy eyes, every onlooker's verdict was "adorable."

One day, when Esther wore her pretty dress, Jadwiga's gorgeous son, Kuba, happened to drop by to inquire about his mother's well-being. It was magic for both. In exuberant Russian, Kuba told her how beautiful she looked. Mother blushed most becomingly, and Jadwiga was delighted.

The next day, Jadwiga carried a note from her son. "Dear Esther," it read, "I shall be honored if you accompany me for high tea at the Ritz Hotel. Would Sunday afternoon suit you? You will make me the happiest man in the world. Jacob Rubinow."

As Mother blushed reading the note, Jadwiga's eyes glowed like a freshly shined samovar.

Esther showed Kuba's note to her parents and sisters.

"He is handsome," Zila said, clapping her hands. "And rich."

"His mother is a bitch," Fanya said.

Elena was horrified. "Fanya, I don't like you using such terrible language."

"I'm sorry, Mama, but everyone in Bialystok says so!"

Esther remained faithful to her employer. "You're wrong. Madame Rubinow is a nice and generous lady."

It was then that Grandfather joined the conversation. "Fanyele, I can forgive Mrs. Rubinow for being strong, if you consider who she's married to. It's no secret that Mark Rubinow is a cruel man, at least he was when he had power. Now she has proven that a woman can be as strong and as shrewd as a man."

Even Mina piped up. "I saw Kuba on the street and he's really handsome."

It was the final word. Esther was given permission to have tea at the Ritz with her future husband.

The Ritz was grand, magnificent, sparkling chandeliers illuminated every person who emerged through the revolving door. Esther gasped, "I've heard about this place. But you must come here often."

Kuba's modesty was seductive. "Yes, sometimes."

A man dressed most elegantly showed them to a table near a window looking across the avenue onto the steeple and cross of Saint Stephen's Church.

They burst out laughing. "Your father should see this," Kuba said.

"Let's not tell him."

They ate something, she wasn't sure what, but the tea was a deep gold and fragrant.

"Mmmm," she inhaled the vapor.

"From London." She was impressed with his knowledge of tea.

My mother was so much in love that all she could do was stare deeply into Kuba's eyes as he regaled her with his Russian adventures. And he thought, she is wonderful, beautiful and intelligent.

The date was a huge success.

The following Sunday, Kuba was invited to Kupiecka Street to meet Esther's parents. She worried about what he might think of her family's humble dwelling. But she needn't have worried. Kuba exuberantly praised their home and vegetable garden.

He knew that it was customary to bring roses. But since you couldn't eat roses, he bought a Belgian chocolate cake at the best bakery in town. After the introductions, he extended the cake to Rebbetzin Rakowski. To his surprise, she didn't budge.

Jacob Meyer stroked his bead. "Yakov, where did you buy this cake?"

"At the Piast Royal Bakery, of course."

"Of course, the finest goyishe bakery in town." The Rabbi managed to project both a smile and a frown, and Kuba didn't know what to make of it. Then came some hesitation, and eyes raised toward the ceiling. I hope he's not asking God for advice, Kuba thought.

Jacob Meyer lowered his eyes. "Yakov, I appreciate your noble intentions, but we cannot have this unkosher cake in our house."

Hoping perhaps to tempt them, Father untied the box to show what they were missing.

"I never saw such a pretty cake," Elena acknowledged.

The Rabbi looked thoughtful. "Here is what we'll do. For you, Yakov, we shall sacrifice a plate and a fork. You can sit here with Esterke on this comfortable sofa and eat the cake. Esterke will watch, but she cannot partake."

The four Rakowski girls and their parents watched as an undaunted Kuba demolished half the cake. They applauded. The rest of the magnificent chocolate creation was thrown out, together with the plate and fork.

For my mother, it was an event to remember.

The wedding was a simple affair held in Grandfather's synagogue, to which members of the congregation brought enough food for the twelve tribes of Israel. The clothes were even more luxurious. Grandmother Jadwiga's Salon came through with the most elaborate bridal gown studded with pearls. Grandmother Elena was gifted a dress in pale green, and Esther's sisters wore pink.

Fanya whispered, "I can vomit from this pink," but the others loved their dresses.

A strange transformation happened to my father after the wedding. He felt a deep respect, perhaps even love, for his father-in-law, Jacob Meyer. It was strange and unexpected. Kuba had made a subconscious decision to pretend that this new man in his life was his real father. To prove this, he asked Jacob Meyer for a prayer shawl, a yarmulke and a prayer book. Thus equipped, he stunned residents of the Jewish Quarter, marching shoulder to shoulder with the Rabbi every Saturday morning for the long synagogue service.

Father rented a grand apartment in the fashionable—and mostly Christian—part of town, Zwirki Wigura Avenue, where Jacob Meyer used to pace in his restless days. So how wonderful was our apartment? It was situated between the Ritz Hotel and the banks of the Bialka River. Across the avenue was a lush park, and to the left the Branicki Palace, owned by the noble family that had founded Bialystok.

It was a beautiful residence. Esther had never seen people living like this. The only other such places she had been to was Jadwiga's salon and the Ritz. But those were public establishments, like places in movies. The rooms here were vast and the ceiling so high it seemed to ascend to the clouds. The salon was as big as Grandfather Jacob Meyer's house, and the number of bedrooms was five. My parents' bedroom alone was the size of the synagogue sanctuary.

The enormous kitchen terrified my mother. I can barely cook, she thought, but with this kind of kitchen they must expect me to become a chef. Moments later she recovered. Nothing bad could happen because she and her husband were breathlessly in love.

On February 11, 1926, my brother, Wolf, was born. Named after Grandmother Elena's father, he was the first grandchild of both the Rakowskis and the Rubinows.

CHAPTER FOUR

My brother entered the world with fanfare and flourish. It was obvious at once that he was a genius. Perhaps that was the reason for his many names: Wolf, Ze'ev, his Hebrew name, Wlodzimierz, his Polish name, Wlodek, his Polish nickname, Vlodimir, his Russian name, and Wowka, his Russian nickname.

The one that stuck was Wowka.

Recorded signs of early genius: At age three, Wowka recognized a false note in a neighbor's violin rendition of a Chopin etude. Conclusion: The child will be a musical prodigy like Glinka or Paderewski. At four, Wowka memorized a Krilov fable about the cricket and the ant. Conclusion: He will be a great poet like Pushkin or Byron.

Soon Wowka acquired three cousins, all boys. The first was Bronek, son of Aunt Fanya and her husband Grisha Kagan. Their marriage was a blessing to Elena and Jacob Meyer, who had felt somewhat ashamed that Esther, a younger daughter, had married before the older Fanya. But Fanya didn't tarry. She met Grisha while working as a bookkeeper in a grain broker's office. He was the older son of a mill owner near Bialystok. Tall and rich, Grisha was sensitive and somewhat bookish.

Fanya said, "I have never seen a man look so good in black-rimmed spectacles."

For a while, a nasty rumor trailed the newlyweds. According to the tale, when Grisha and Fanya fell in love, he had been seriously courting another young lady. The gossip continued with the sordid account of Grisha unceremoniously ditching his girlfriend, who, in an act of revenge, threw herself under the train in which the young couple traveled on their honeymoon. Whatever the truth, the scandalous story was avidly whispered by maidens in the Jewish Quarter, and matrons lunching at the Ritz. The Jewish gossipers wondered that both Wowka and Bronek looked conveniently Aryan.

The other cousin was Misha Rubinow, son of Uncle Ossya and his wife Mira. The third was Tolek Rakowski, born to my uncle Lev and his wife, Tanya Graveh. Lev had fulfilled his dream of marrying a rich girl, in this case an extremely rich girl, and a nice person to boot. Old man Graveh owned several apartment buildings in the best part of Bialystok, as well as a sizable chunk of commercial real estate that he was renting out to textile factories.

But there was something odd about Tanya. She possessed the most enormous, wild-looking eyes in Bialystok. They were like two huge eggs floating in her sockets in opposite directions, as if one roamed in search of its mate.

It's worthwhile mentioning that by the time Wowka was born, my parents employed a live-in maid, Aniusia, who occupied one of the back rooms, and a laundress who came in daily to scrub sheets and towels, then hang them in the inner courtyard, where children played far from street traffic.

A couple of years after Wowka's birth, a stranger turned up in front of Grandfather Jacob Meyer's door. Tall and stocky, he had a broad face that bore a glowing purple birthmark on its right cheek. He was tired and unshaven, signs that he had traveled for a long time in hard circumstances. He introduced himself as David Sorochkin, son of the Chief Rabbi of Moscow, on the run from the NKVD, the People's Commissariat for Military Affairs. Bialystok, only 40 kilometers from Belarus, was the closest Polish city to the Soviet Union.

David washed up and devoured meatloaf, potatoes and cooked kohlrabi with a hunger typical of anyone escaping the Soviet Secret Police. Then, with a luxurious "Ah," he proceeded to recount his incredible story. "The more I look back, the stranger it appears. I was in my last year at Moscow University's Department of Mechanical Engineering. I had good grades, my parents were happy, and I stayed away from political activity. So, I was stunned when I received a summons from the NKVD.

"I walked into an ugly gray building, as all Soviet buildings tend to be. They directed me to a room with a cheap desk, behind which sat a bureaucrat with ordinary features, like the kind Gogol likes to describe. Prominently displayed on the table was a file with the name "D. Sorochkin" written boldly in black pen. The man did not look at me or introduce himself, but opened the file and leafed through it, frowning. I began to sweat. I beg the young ladies to excuse my language. Suddenly, the functionary put a heavy finger in the middle of a page and said in a loud voice, 'Aha!

You are David Sorochkin, younger son of what you people call a religious leader, Rabbi Abraham Sorochkin?'

"I replied, 'Yes.'

"The man raised his voice. 'Do not answer me! Only listen. So you are twenty-five years old, and in a few months you will graduate from the finest university in the world, the People's University of Moscow, an education for which the Soviet Union is generously paying—although so far, you have made no sacrifices or contributions to the welfare of the Motherland.'

"I felt my arms shaking, but tried to appear calm. The apparatchik continued, 'It says here that you have excellent grades. It must be a trick of your religion that makes you smart. I see that you go to your church, or whatever you call it, on Friday nights. But you missed Friday, October 13, because you were out in a dance hall with Clara Menkova. Pretty girl.' At this point my composure was out of the window, and the Commissar noticed my anxiety. Then he delivered a final blow. 'A remarkable stain you have on your cheek, Comrade Sorochkin. Is it an accident or a birthmark? Oh, no, no, you need not answer.'

"He stood up and extended his hand. 'You may go now, David Abramovich. Have a nice day.'"

At this point in the story, David was pacing. He wiped his forehead and shrugged with bewilderment. "I returned home a broken man. It is possible that the NKVD were playing with me. For them it's a blood sport. Most likely, it was a warning that they meant to recruit me to work for them and denounce members of the Jewish community."

The visitor touched his cheek, a movement he had repeated several times in the course of his narrative. "My mark is a giveaway.

They could find me anywhere. So, I packed a rucksack with a few necessities, my parents gave me all the money they had available, and my father convinced me to take his prayer shawl, which has been in the family for generations. 'Take it to freedom,' he said."

David opened his rucksack and withdrew the voluminous tallis, its top and edges embroidered with gold thread, the fabric replete with the yellow stains of past generations' sweat. He spread it on the kitchen table for everyone to admire. "I left my house and started out on foot toward the Polish border. The first address my father had given me was yours, Rabbi Rakowski."

"My son-in-law Jacob made the same trip."

Zila's eyes sparkled. For her, it was a miracle and an omen that a stranger had somehow walked into their house.

Zila's joy was reinforced in the coming days, as David began singing arias from Russian operas in a sublime baritone. It is well known that the most stellar baritone solo is from Tchaikovsky's "Eugene Onegin," in which Lensky, a young man in love, fights a duel with the hero, Onegin. Everyone cries listening to Lensky's ode to his beloved before his red blood gushes into the whiteness of St. Petersburg snow. While David sang, everyone cried and wished Lensky had killed Onegin instead.

David, son of the Moscow rabbi, would have made Tchaikovsky proud. And since the streets in the Jewish Quarter were narrow and the wooden houses small and drafty, David's singing filled Kupiecka Street. Neighbors poured out of their homes and headed for Number 14. People oohed and aahed, and women who understood no Russian still cried, because David's voice was so romantic.

That Friday night, Rabbi Rakowski walked towards his

synagogue as usual, this time accompanied by his atheist son-in-law and his future son-in law David, resplendent in his father's tallis. And when this stranger burst out in the famous cantorial chant Adon Olam—Master of the World—men who had heard it all their lives cried for the first time.

Back home, Grandfather turned to David. "Tell me, my son, why do you want to be a mechanical engineer?"

"Because I like cars and engines."

Hearing the ridiculous statement, Grandfather cast his eyes to heaven and said no more.

Zila heard music in every word David uttered. Dispensing with custom, Elena and Jacob Meyer allowed the pair to go to town without having to account for their whereabouts. Mina, meanwhile, was despondent, because her parents made it clear that she could not accompany her sister while she was out with the man she intended to marry.

In the middle of so much joy, David's mood took a sudden plunge. He refused to sing or go out. Instead, he sat in the kitchen, morose, his hand pressed to his purple cheek. "I have revealed myself too much," he moaned. "I am certain that now the NKVD is on my trail, and within days I shall be arrested and thrown into the Lubyanka." This was the most brutal prison in Moscow.

Zila cried, and so did Mina. Grandfather realized that David was hysterical, although he knew many men and women who were hysterical at the mention of the Soviet prison.

"There is a solution," he said. "My sister Puah is an important Zionist leader. She runs a farm near Warsaw, where she prepares young girls for settlement in Palestine. When the next group graduates, she will personally escort them to Palestine. So, here is our plan: David, if you want, I shall call my sister and see when she'll be ready."

"Oh, yes!" Zila and David cried in unison.

As it turned out, the next group of girls would board the German liner, Die Valkyrie, in two weeks, in the Polish port of Gdansk, known in German as Danzig.

"I asked her to include Zila and David in the group," Grandpa announced. He noticed Mina bowling like a stifled kitten. "And Mina too, of course."

On Friday night, my grandparents sat down to the Sabbath meal with their departing children. Present were also Esther and Kuba, with Wowka, then four and reciting Sabbath blessings he had memorized.

A very chipper David said to my father, "Kuba, you should send money to Palestine to buy yourself an orchard. They are cheap now, and you will own a piece of the Promised Land."

Father grinned and spread his arms to encircle his family. "I have the Promised Land right here in Poland," he said.

CHAPTER FIVE

Grandmother Jadwiga was pleased. She listed in her mind her favorite son's achievements: desirable wife, huge income, apartment in an exclusive neighborhood far from the Jewish Quarter, a child who seemed extraordinarily smart, a maid, a laundress and more. Now, the time was ripe for Kuba and Fira to meet Bialystok's Jewish society. It was easier for Grandmother to navigate the city since she had moved her residence from the relatively modest three bedrooms to a glittering five-bedroom with an enormous kitchen perfect for catering, and a salon suited for entertaining. Unlike her ultra-feminine dress shop, her new residence was slick, almost austere.

On a Saturday night in June, Jadwiga invited Bialystok's Who's Who to her apartment to dine with her and meet the handsome young couple. Indeed, Fira and Kuba looked like poster children for the progress that educated and rich young Jews had made in newly independent Poland. Mother excelled in subdued glamour, while Father delighted the ladies with his looks, and the men with his knowledge of world textile markets.

Mother picked up the social baton, and a month later hosted a dinner for eight in their new apartment. To make sure that nothing went amiss, Jadwiga sent over her cook, who taught Mother the difference between bordelaise and béarnaise sauces. In the months to come she would learn more haute cuisine.

Another source of social advancement came from retired general, Count Stefan Wola Krzysztoporska, (from here on to be known as General Wola), uncle of the young playboys in Paris. The General, who had lost his wife a year earlier, had found himself at loose ends. His children were scattered throughout Poland and abroad. He had rented out his much-too-large country villa in Podlasie, and was looking for lodgings in the city. Mother described him as "a darling man," with a voluminous white moustache reminiscent of Polish mountain men who appeared in travel advertisements.

Father agreed to offer the General a room until he made some permanent arrangements for himself. The General was in no hurry. Like all men, he fell in love with my mother and proceeded to introduce his benefactors to the local Polish nobility, a circle few Jews could penetrate. The Polish men accepted Mother with open arms, so to speak. With her blond hair, blue eyes and perfect Polish diction, she could have been married to any of them.

The noble Polish ladies were not as happy with my mother. Since many of them were Grandmother's clients, they had heard the gossip that her son had married one of the seamstresses. Couldn't this very handsome rich boy do better than this shameless hussy, flirting with their husbands?

The next step in my parents' social education was to learn bridge. Father's mathematical mind absorbed the game flawlessly, but Mother limped along and was soon relegated to a foursome of semi-beginners, all ladies. The games were boisterous, wine and cognac flowed, and the men and some women—but rarely Mother—discussed the troubling events in Germany.

One Saturday morning after synagogue, Grandfather asked his almost-son Kuba, "Don't you think, Yakov, that it's time to send Wolf to cheder?" Cheder is the term for a Jewish religious school for young boys.

Father, who had never contemplated this future for Wowka, wondered how to disagree without being disagreeable. "Well, sir, I really don't think that we would like for Wolf to go in this direction."

Grandfather appeared crestfallen; but, of course, he wasn't. The cheder request was an opening gambit. Now Grandfather appeared to lapse into deep thought. "We still must find a way for a smart boy like Wolf to know Torah and the holidays and Hebrew prayers, maybe even speak Hebrew. My sister Puah tells me that soon there will be a Jewish state in what is now Palestine." He stopped and breathed hard, though he was not at all winded. "I tell you something, Yakov; I joined a Zionist party."

"You? Really?"

"Yes. I am now a member of the Mizrahi, the Religious Zionist movement. If we have a Jewish state, we in the Mizrahi will make sure that it is run by the laws of the Torah." He straightened his back. "Now, what about Wolf?"

Father returned to the subject reluctantly. "There must be a way for him to receive a normal education and also, somehow, do the religious thing."

"Exactly! It's Hebrew day school. Ours is better than the one in Warsaw, though they have ten times the number of Jews. In this school, he will learn all the general subjects in Polish. You know, literature, history, mathematics. But on top of that, Hebrew and the Bible."

"This is good, very good," Father smiled, certain that he had won.

Wowka was six when he was marched off to Hebrew Day School, where the tuition was high and therefore attractive to many less religious Jews. Two traits distinguished my brother from other children. First, his ability to memorize. This is how the little boy explained it: "I hate to carry books around, because I keep losing them. So, I put it in my head where it stays." Second: he was the tallest boy his age. This forced teachers to sit him in the back row. Good for the teacher because Ze'ev, as he was known in Hebrew, was a disrupter, calling out words before the teacher could, all the while maintaining an air of superiority.

Summers in Bialystok were hot and dusty. Automobiles mingled with horse-driven buggies of farmers bringing vegetables and eggs to market. Other peddlers would ride in from Belarus, our border Soviet state, buying used clothes and housewares, then selling them to people with a chronic shortage of everything.

In Bialystok, schools were out, and most rich men sent their families to the mountains. The Tatrys is a scenic mountain range, where the air is sweet, and the water runs lazily in the brooks, so blue and translucent that you could spend days submerged in it.

In 1932, Father rented a small villa for a month, where Mother and Wowka spent the summer vacation swimming in the lake, riding ponies and eating fresh fruits and vegetables. This area is renowned for the best cheeses, sour cream and eggs. Wowka was an excellent swimmer, but most ponies were too small for him, so the resort owners found him a docile mare. Father came up to visit whenever he could and was delighted with the neighbors, a friendly bunch who had left their troubles behind and whose conversation was breezy and superficial. It had all gone so well that the following summer, Father booked the villa for two months.

But in 1934, their summer vacation was cut short. Three weeks into their stay, Father brought his wife and son back to Bialystok. They were no longer jolly or smiling. Mother was in tears, and spent a week wandering around the apartment like a ghost. When Grandfather and Elena inquired what was wrong, Father said that she had caught bronchitis in the mountains and needed to come home early. Eight-year-old Wowka screamed vile curses at his father, and was rewarded with blows on his naked behind with the leather belt on which Father sharpened his razor.

By the start of the school year in September, and soon after the advent of the Jewish New Year, an air of measured calm returned to the Rubinow home. The atmosphere of rage subsided, giving way to a quiet air of discontent.

Then, in the spring of 1935, Mother became pregnant with me.

CHAPTER SIX

t is hard to explain why wealthy European Jews, especially women, were so obsessed with music. The thinking probably went that if Mrs. Menuhin and Mrs. Heifetz had the genius boys Yehudi and Yascha, why couldn't Mrs. Rubinow have a musical prodigy called Wowka?

So, my brother was made to fiddle at age four. He played well, but not brilliantly. Besides, he was lazy. His eyes did not glow at the mention of practice. If possible, he hid inside dirty sheets in the laundry room.

To motivate her son, Mother found a new teacher who presented Wowka with a miniature violin. At first, he liked it, but then he grew bored. By the time he was seven, they sat him on the piano stool. The newest teacher, who played piano at Grandmother Jadwiga's soirees, congratulated Wowka on his "proficient" play. The piano lessons continued until the summer of 1934, when Mother and Wowka returned abruptly from their sojourn in the mountains.

Becoming pregnant again gave Mother a second chance to

produce a musical genius. If so, she picked the wrong child. Oh, how hard she tried! My musical education started in the womb. In there, I was exposed to the best classical music. Mother carried me to performances of the Bialystok Philharmonic, and to Warsaw with Father and Grandmother Jadwiga for a performance of "Tosca" with the visiting Paris Opera. And there was more. Aunt Sonya, now a substitute violinist with the Berlin Philharmonic, sent recordings of Beethoven and Mozart for my embryonic delectation. With the package, incidentally, was a message saying that her husband Miron was still a translator in Von Ribbentrop's Foreign Office.

Somewhere Mother obtained a recording of American jazz that prompted the first contractions. Mother was delighted. The fetus was responding to music! That summer, with me still unborn, Grandmother Jadwiga was diagnosed with breast cancer. Father was devastated. His mother told him calmly that she had had a great life and desired to go in peace. Heaven is not my choice," she said. "I shall be too lonely there. I should like to merrily burn in hell with all my friends."

But Father would have none of it. He rented a limousine, hired a nurse, and told his very pregnant wife that he would be back as soon as his mother was well enough to travel. Father stayed away for two months, rarely telephoning. His correspondence amounted to two postcards. When he finally returned, unshaven and bleary-eyed, he arrived in the limousine alongside his mother's casket.

They buried Grandmother Jadwiga in the Bagnowka Cemetery, the largest and oldest Jewish cemetery in Eastern Poland. Her husband, Grandfather Mark, stood with his oldest son Ossya and his wife Mira. Father was alone, since Mother was in no condition to withstand such freezing weather.

My grandmother Elena did not wait for me, either. She suffered a fatal coronary on Yom Kippur. Everyone was impressed by how well she had timed her death. You see, religious Jews believe that only the righteous are privileged to die on Yom Kippur. Ridiculous, don't you think that the rewards for righteousness should be life, not death?

Finally, here I am! January 3, 1936. Bialystok yentes who had gossiped for years as to why the Rabbi's daughter did not have more children, were at last deprived of their juiciest subject.

My mother was determined to name me after a romantic heroine from a Russian novel, Natasha or Tatyana. But Grandfather thought differently. "Thank God it's a girl!" he enthused. "The first girl in the Rakowski or Rubinow families. We must name her Rachel, after my saintly mother, the Rebettsin Rachel Rakowski."

Oy! Mother was mortified to have a daughter with such a common Jewish name, after a grandmother whom she remembered as a dour, black-clad figure. Aunt Fanya helpfully suggested that "Rala," a romantic nickname.

Back to the music! Following on the musical education in the womb, Mother installed a record player in my nursery, from which wafted gentle sounds of Tchaikovsky and Chopin. After a month of celestial tunes, I began vomiting, not in a genteel fashion, but as a hostile deluge. Whatever I ate blew out of my mouth and nostrils. Mother, scared that I might die of malnutrition, stuffed me with additional portions of scrambled eggs and sour cream. With this intake of food, I had more raw material to disgorge. Mother deployed even sweeter music, which made me sicker.

The maid quit, tired of cleaning up after me. Mother handled me by herself, because Father was unwilling to go near a vomiting child. He went looking for a new maid and found our Marysia. To make sure that this one stayed, they also hired a governess. Miss Julie was a fragile-looking Jewish girl, with light brown curls and a heart murmur. She combed her hair in a washerwoman's style that was very becoming and made her look even more vulnerable.

Somehow the music stopped. So did the vomiting. I grew into a normal human child. Except for one deficiency: I am tone deaf.

After Grandmother Jadwiga's funeral, her sons Kuba and Ossya were confronted with the responsibility of caring for their father Mark, now in his eighties. My parents invited Ossya and Mira to our home for dinner to discuss the matter. Ossya arrived alone. He sat down, but refused to eat.

"Look at the way you live," he said, pointing at the Persian rug. "Your rooms, your servants. Compared to you, Mira and I are paupers."

Mother tried to defuse the situation. "Ossya, please have some brisket and mashed potatoes."

Mother's soothing words further irritated Ossya. "Yes, brisket. Cooked by your maid, no doubt. What I am trying to say is that I cannot take care of Father. I don't have the money or the time. You have both."

Father stood up and so did Ossya: two tall men glaring at each other.

"You son of a bitch!" Father said through clenched teeth. "The monster loves you. He never hit you or screamed at you. And now you have the temerity to tell me that you want no part of him!"

"Kuba, please," Mother entreated.

Father ignored her. "Ossya," he continued, "get the hell out of my house, and don't come back!"

That week, they moved Grandfather Mark from the apartment he had shared with his wife to a smaller one in a neighborhood populated by teachers and artists. It was near a little park where Grandfather took daily walks, beating a marching staccato with a hand-carved mountain cane. In all seasons except summer, he wore his trademark camel hair overcoat that he had purchased in Paris. He walked erect, eyes looking ahead, paying no attention to passers-by.

When Mother suggested that they invite Grandfather for dinner once a week, Father said blisteringly, "Over my dead body!"

Since Mother grew up in a compassionate home, each week she and Marysia carried baskets of potted chicken, noodle pudding and soups to Grandfather Rubinow's apartment. He thanked Mother each time and complimented her on her cooking.

This arrangement lasted until tragedy struck. Grandfather Mark suffered a stroke that withered his right arm and left him speechless. In the hospital, the doctor explained that he might recover some motion, but no speech.

"One thing is clear, Mr. Rubinow," the doctor told my father. "Your father can no longer live alone."

Back home, my parents argued over Grandfather's fate. "Let's put him in the best nursing home in Bialystok," Father suggested.

Mother was shocked. "Jews don't send their parents to die in a nursing home. The only people in the Jewish Home for the Aged are the ones without children. And besides, my father will never allow it."

"So, what do you suggest?"

"He must come to live with us."

"Nice. And what do you suggest we tell General Wola?"

The General appeared as if on cue, dressed for the outdoors. "Fira and I discussed the situation," he announced. "My daughter has been pestering me for a long time to come and live with them in my country estate. I meant to tell you this."

There was nothing more for Father to say. When he parted from them, the General told my parents, "Please remember that I still have friends in the Army. We can help you if the need arises. Never forget that you are Polish citizens, and the Republic owes you protection."

Mother laughed. "What can possibly happen to us?"

So, Grandfather Mark came to live with us, accompanied by a male nurse, Mr. Zymek, a short man with a wrestler's physique and a moustache that curled up at the ends. The two settled in General Wola's room.

The stroke had rendered Grandfather's body so rigid that he was forced to shuffle, holding on to Mr. Zymek. But worse than his physical impairment was his inability to speak. Humiliation and rage glowed in his eyes. He emitted a variety of guttural sounds, as if a scratchy music box had been implanted in his larynx.

Grandfather became our household ghost. I felt his presence even when he was out of sight. I knew that he was my other grandfather, and that I should be nice to him. But I didn't know how. So, I smiled at him with what I believed was an expression of friendliness. He did not smile back. He just stood there, staring at me with his large moist eyes.

One day, Grandfather fell during his daily walk in the park with Mr. Zymek. The strong man carried his bleeding patient upstairs. Father called for an ambulance, which transported Grandfather to the hospital accompanied by Mr. Zymek. Mother and Father drove behind.

The next day Grandfather died from bleeding in his brain. Zymek said that before he died, he tried to say something that sounded like "Yo," the first syllable of his wife's Hebrew name. Father's eyes filled with tears.

After the funeral, people gathered in our apartment to observe shiva, the seven days of mourning. Ossya and Mira arrived with my cousin Misha. I was confused by the presence of so many people dressed in black and whispering to each other. My governess, Miss Julie, brought me a piece of torte from the table laden with food. The mourners stayed too long. And they would come for another seven days.

Midway through the week, Uncle Ossya turned to Father. "Kuba, as the firstborn, I'm entitled to Father's camel hair overcoat. It's the only thing I'll have to remember him by."

Father's eyes darkened with fury. "You, you—!" He could barely contain himself. "The overcoat is mine, for reasons I shall not be so crude as to say in front of all these people."

The mourners, smelling a family quarrel, filed out. Mother and Grandfather Jacob Meyer attempted to make peace between the warring brothers. Suddenly, Ossya peeled off from the group, ran toward the closet, grabbed the overcoat and advanced toward the door. Light as a panther, Father leapt up and blocked it.

Grandfather Jacob Meyer finally intervened. "It really is a fine overcoat, and we should hate to do a King Solomon judgment and cut it in half. Instead, let me take it home with me, and each of you can come over and visit it."

The brothers relinquished their hold on the overcoat, and Grandfather Jacob Meyer carried it off to Number 14, Kupiecka Street.

CHAPTER SEVEN

I loved it when people said, "Rala, you are adorable." But what I hated was when they said, "You look so delicious I could eat you up." Someone wanting to eat me up was disgusting. Then there was, "You look just like your father." This must have been true, because no one ever said that I looked like my mother.

All these are nice things people say about me. So why does my brother hate me?

I first learned this truth when I was two years old. That evening the four of us were alone in the apartment, because Mother had given Miss Julie three days off to travel to Warsaw and see her fiancé, who was a musician and "lived in a garret." Mother loved struggling artists who lived in garrets.

"It's so romantic," she would say. Marysia, our maid, had gone home to her parents' village and was due back the following day.

The telephone rang, and Mother answered. When she hung up, she told Father that the Dromans, one of their bridge couples, needed them to fill in for someone else. "I'll call Fanya and ask her to come over and take care of Rala,"

57

Wowka was indignant. "Why not me? I can take care of Rala. I shall soon have my Bar Mitzvah."

"Absolutely not!" Father barked.

But Mother smiled. "Kuba, listen. This is a perfect opportunity for the children to find closeness."

"I want this very much," Wowka insisted.

Father had no choice. "We'll be back very soon," he told my brother with a scowl.

The moment they left, Wowka ran into his room and returned with his brand-new ice skates. He dangled them in front of me. I got into the spirit and clapped my hands.

"Beautiful, aren't they? Our venerable pater familias refused to buy them for me. But Mother does what I want. She also bought me the watch and the fountain pen."

Wowka dragged my crib from my parents' bedroom into the salon. "So, you can watch," he explained.

He threw off his shoes and strapped on the ice skates. Rolling back the Persian rug, he revealed Mother's and Marysia's precious wooden floor, buffed to a glorious sheen. Then he scooted over to the gramophone and put on a record.

"Now, dear child," he said, "prepare yourself for the first exquisite event of your life!"

In tune with the music, my brother proceeded to glide along like a clumsy giraffe. "Padam, padam, padam! This tune is 'The Firebird,' by Igor Stravinsky. But, as we all know, you are tone deaf. Padam! You will never experience the pleasures of music."

I knew nothing about Igor Stravinsky, but I knew about Mother's cherished floor. As Wowka was skating on its slick veneer, the wood was quickly transformed into a mass of splits and gashes. Abuse of the floor must have distressed me so much that I began to scream in an attempt to climb out of the crib. Wowka paid me no attention. I rattled the spokes of my crib. Nothing. I looked up. My brother was not actually skating, so much as savagely attacking the floor.

Somehow, I managed to throw myself out of the crib and onto the pockmarked wood, at which point an errant splinter imbedded itself in my cheek. I sat there screaming and watching my blood spreading on my nightgown. Wowka fell into a chair, breathing hard, laughing.

At that moment my parents walked in. Seeing the disaster, Mother uttered an incredulous "Oh, my God!"

Wowka stared at Father defiantly and was rewarded with a ringing slap across his face. I was still wailing, while Mother lamented the floor and Father screamed at Wowka for his transgressions.

Suddenly they noticed me on the floor, upon which Mother uttered another, "Oh, my God!"

She ran toward me, her shock turning into dismay. "Kuba, the child is hurt!"

Father rushed toward me as well, and Wowka used the opportunity to run out of the apartment. Mother washed off my face and applied iodine to my cheek, which hurt so much I became hysterical.

She hugged and kissed me some more, then said the magic words, "Let me make some cocoa."

Father, meanwhile, was left alone with his mounting rage. He ran into the bedroom and retrieved his leather belt. Thus armed, he sprinted out of the apartment in search of his son. He connected with Wowka in the park across the street and dragged him back by his shirt collar. Then he stood my brother up in the middle of the ravaged floor and landed the strap across his back.

In pain and triumph, Wowka screamed out, "Did you imagine that I stayed here to take care of your brat?"

"You hooligan!" Father retorted, hitting him even harder.

"You miserable tyrant!" Wowka hissed.

I was drinking cocoa in the kitchen, while Mother observed the scene with pain and disbelief. When Wowka's cries increased beyond her ability to endure them, she ran into the salon and grabbed Father's arm. "Stop it! You are injuring the child!"

"He is not a child. A child does not have so much evil in him."

In a sorrowful voice, Mother said, "You are becoming your father."

With this, Father let go, and Wowka scampered away to his room. That night I was frightened from an evil spirit in the air.

Two busy weeks followed. A crew of workmen repaired the damaged floor and miraculously restored it to its original glory. Mother and Marysia almost cried at the sight of the floor's perfection.

While all this was going on, my parents barely noticed that I was no longer repeating words, but forming sentences. I invented for myself a brilliant game. For example: One day Marysia and the laundress were talking, when I overheard: "Mrs. Rubinow's sister Fanya gained weight. She has such a pretty face, but she loves sweets too much."

I made an effort to remember every word, and when Fanya, Grisha and Bronek came to dinner, I announced, "Marysia and Bronia said that Aunt Fanya gained weight." Then I laughed uproariously because I was so clever.

Soon enough I learned what adults mean by the words, "Don't say it in front of the child." Bronia and Marysia were careful to say nothing interesting in front of me, so I let them be.

My next scheme was to make Mother happy. She loved Russian poetry. Her favorite was Pushkin, a poet who had been dead forever. I asked Mother to read me some poetry, which I memorized and repeated back to her. She looked stunned. Then she kissed and hugged me so much I almost choked. "You are a very smart child. Maybe not quite like Wowka, but very smart indeed."

The discovery of my talent gave Mother an idea. On Wednesday, which was bridge night in our apartment, she dressed me in my best pink frock, stood me up on a chair in the center of the salon, and told me to recite the opening verses of Pushkin's Eugene Onegin.

People clapped and teared up.

"The child is a genius!" cried one lovely woman. It was time to curtsy. "Oh, she is so adorable!"

It was November 1938, and preparations for Wowka's Bar Mitzvah were in full swing. My grandfather worried that his oldest son, my Uncle Marek, might not be able to attend. By then, Marek Rakowski was one of the most famous Yiddish writers in Poland. So why would this remarkable man not attend his nephew's Bar Mitzvah? Because, as in his youth, Marek was in jail. This jail was the most brutal in Europe, a concentration camp called Bereza Kartuska, built by the Polish government for political prisoners. Writers and artists were incarcerated at will on the pretext of "spreading Communist propaganda." The prison's name was spoken in whispers, as people in it were never charged, given a trial or a sentence. They simply disappeared.

But just as they had jailed Marek for no reason, they let him out seemingly on a whim. Back in Warsaw, a very thin Marek reconnected with his friends. Then, for the first time in his life, he got lucky. He fell in love with Dr. Mary Bandrimer, a successful dentist, and she with him.

Soon Grandfather was reading aloud Marek's telegram. "Free man in love!" it read. "Arriving with my wife Dr. Mary Bandrimer, who bought me a fancy suit for this occasion!"

On my third birthday, January 3, 1939, one month before Wowka's Bar Mitzvah, my parents gave me a splendid gift: my own custom-made overcoat of gray gabardine lined with beaver. It also had a beaver collar and a muff hanging on a black velvet string around my neck. In the upper pocket Mother had sewn a red chiffon handkerchief.

"Red wards off the evil eye," she explained.

Father raised his eyebrows. "I can't believe you're as superstitious as a Russian peasant!"

I clapped my hands. "No child in Bialystok has as beautiful a coat as this. I am so special!"

Because it was so close to the Bar Mitzvah, Grandfather started bringing around his minyan, the requisite minimum of ten Jewish men without whom prayers cannot begin. They spent many hours in our salon praying, chanting and solving the world's problems. Their appetite for cake was enormous. Father had to buy it at a kosher bakery and show it to them in the original wrapping. Not trusting Mother, they brought along their own plates. They did allow her to serve them tea in glasses. Mugs were not kosher; neither was pouring sugar. Sugar lumps were their preference. Why? Grandfather had an answer: "The Lord said you must sip your tea through something sweet, like a lump of sugar."

Father asked, "How many of these commandments are there?"

"Six-hundred thirteen, my dear son-in-law. But I don't perform them all. You see," he said, pointing to his sugar-sucking congregants, "my people are more religious than I am."

In the midst of this heightened religious discourse, I waltzed in, resplendent in my new coat. Grandfather was annoyed. "Esterke, you cannot have a child parading in fur when people are dying all over the world."

Mother seemed perplexed. "Papa, people are always dying somewhere."

I began to cry. I didn't want the coat if people were dying because of it. But my anxiety passed when Grandfather picked me up in his arms. "Isn't Rala the most beautiful little girl in Bialystok?"

His friends showered me with compliments, so no more tears. As I made my exit, I found Wowka at the door. He pulled me over. "These men are here for me, not you," he sneered. "They are here because next month will be my Bar Mitzvah, so don't forget it."

I slithered by him. I was so happy with Grandfather's bearded entourage that I put cake on their plates and handed it to each of them, also a lump of sugar near their tea. I even distributed napkins. I was somehow convinced that without me, this minyan couldn't pray.

After the guests departed, Wowka called me over. "You know that you're my favorite sister!" he lifted me in the air. We sat down together on the piano bench. "Look, Rala, I have to warn you. Men with long beards are evil. The Devil dispatches them to invade earth, become friendly with little girls like you, so they can kidnap them and drag them off to their dungeons. There the girls are boiled in steaming cauldrons."

I put my hand on my mouth and cried, "But Grandfather has a beard!"

"This man that you think is our grandfather—is really someone else, an impostor."

"What is an impostor?"

"Someone who pretends to be our grandfather, but isn't! The Devil sent an evil substitute and made him look like Grandfather."

By this point, I was shaking. Kidnapped, boiled, oh my God!

The next day, when Grandfather and his minyan arrived, I screamed in terror and fled. I did not return until Wowka told me they were gone. This scene was repeated for several days, until Grandfather caught me from behind, put me on his knee and demanded an explanation.

"Are you really my grandfather?"

Mother joined us. "Rala, he is my father, which means he is your grandfather."

I closed my eyes. "Wowka says that bearded men are evil, and that the Devil sent them from hell to kidnap little girls, throw them in their dungeons, and boil them in a pot for dinner."

Father's eyes filled with rage. "The black-hearted hooligan!" He headed to his bedroom to fetch his belt.

Grandfather caught up with him. "No, Yakov, not now. Not before the Bar Mitzvah."

Father relented. "Father-in-law, you have always been a just man."

Then it came to pass: The greatest event in mankind's history, the Bar Mitzvah of Wolf Rubinow! It was a clear and sunny day, only forty-five degrees, an extraordinary gift for mid-February. Wowka stood in Grandfather's synagogue in the Jewish Quarter, flanked by his father and grandfather. The Bar Mitzvah boy and his father were of the same height: six-foot-three.

Wowka had memorized the complete service: the blessings, the chants, the Torah portion, and the prophetic segment that followed it. His speech to the congregation was intelligent and thought-provoking.

"Dear Grandfather, beloved Father, my gracious mother, my aunts and uncles and cousins, as our people say, blessed art Thou Oh Lord, who gave us life and sustained us and allowed us to reach this day. I thank the Almighty for my little sister, Rachel, named after my great-grandmother, the righteous lady Rebbetzin Rachel Rakowski.

"I am proud to be a Jew, as our ancestors have carried our traditions through two thousand years of persecution. Today I stand before you to declare that I have complete faith in our God and in the wise men, many of them my ancestors"—here Grandfather wiped a tear— "who had guided us with wisdom and love."

"He wrote it all himself," Mother whispered to her sister Fanya, as they sat in the women's balcony looking down with joy. "Next in line is Bronek's Bar Mitzvah." The sisters hugged each other and cried.

You normally do not applaud in the synagogue, but this was the first Bar Mitzvah for their rebbe, so what the hell—excuse the expression—the congregation erupted in thunderous applause.

The newly released political prisoner, my atheist Uncle Marek, was smiling, draped in a tallis, with a yarmulke on his dome. It was a surprise to learn that he knew the prayers, though he had never acknowledged it. His wife, Dr. Mary, sat with the women in the balcony, wearing a beautiful blue dress and a brooch with diamonds.

After the evening service, the congregation was invited to our home for the greatest Bar Mitzvah feast in Bialystok's history. As Grandfather's position dictated, the poorest in his congregation were treated with respect—though not hugged or kissed by my parents, as were their rich and assimilated friends, among them the bridge players and other textile mill owners. As a tribute to Father, many ladies wore four-year-old Madame Jadwiga originals.

Speaking of dresses, mine was the best. On his last trip to Warsaw, Father had bought me a knitted navy outfit. The skirt was fluffy, with buttons at the waist, and the top had buttonholes, so you buttoned the top to the skirt. Grandfather's flock and their plain-looking wives separated themselves from the assimilated Jews and the few Christians.

The food was laid out on a table as long as a snake: roasted chicken, brisket, a gigantic turkey looking menacingly alive, mashed potatoes, latkes, kugel, and a disgusting fish stuffed inside with more fish. The fish lying on its side stared at the ravenous guests with a glistening fishy eye. The only vegetable was cut cucumbers with mint, covered with oil and vinegar. The dish was called "misery," though no one knew why.

Wowka walked around the room, smiling and speaking to people. They adored him.

Your speech was wonderful, Wolf.

What a talent you have with words!

You have a memory like the Rock of Gibraltar.

The men surrounded Father, exclaiming, "Mr. Rubinow, you must be so proud of your son!"

I sat on Grandfather's knee, munching on challah with raisins. Actually, I was playing with the challah, which I was not supposed to do because people in a place called India went hungry. Never mind. I began separating the raisins from the challah, stacking them in small hills. When I had a fine stack of raisins, I started counting them out loud in Yiddish,

Some of Wowka's admirers turned to me. "Look at you counting! You are almost as smart as your brother. Too bad girls cannot be rabbis."

I was disappointed that no one had noticed my dress. But they must! I climbed up on the table, unbuttoned my skirt, and let it drop. I danced on the table in my white stockings and black lacquered slippers, waving my skirt in the air. People applauded and cheered.

"Beautiful dress Ralichka," they cried, "beautiful dress!"

From where I stood on top of the table, I could see outside

onto the avenue. It was February 11, 1939, and snowing hard.

CHAPTER EIGHT

"So many crows in the sky," Mother said. "It's frightening."

It was nighttime in mid-September 1939, and we were riding in a horse and buggy on a road cluttered with refugees. The ground and the trudging humans looked grey, while the sky was pewter. The fast-moving black objects above us conveyed a heightened menace.

Wowka giggled: "Mama, what you see in the sky are not crows, but German aircraft monitoring our every step. If they want to, they can kill us in a minute."

Shaking with fear, Mother responded angrily, "I forbid you to say this, certainly not in front of the child."

I smiled. The child. That's me. Though, truly, I had no idea what my brother had said. Coming from him, though, it was probably bad.

So how did it come to pass that Mother, Wowka, Marysia and I were on this road escaping from Bialystok to Marysia's village, Nowa Polana? Simple: the Germans attacked Poland, and no one knew where was safe. In a situation like this, people think that the best place to hide is somewhere else. In our case, it was Marysia's parents' home. Despite the danger, Father stayed in the city to protect his business.

Father had summoned a limousine with his favorite driver, Mr. Witold, and assigned him to drive us to Nowa Polana. That was the first part of our trip, which ended when Mr. Witold ran out of petrol that left the five of us stranded on the side of the road, watching tired refugees straggling by.

Not everyone was on foot. Here and there were horse-driven buggies.

"Aha!" cried Mr. Witold, with what we considered unmerited joy. He pulled over the first unoccupied buggy and crossed himself before the driver. Marysia also crossed herself. I was about to cross myself, but Mother pulled down my arm.

The planes flew lower, and we could hear the engines going grrrrr. Everyone fell to the ground. No bombs, however; the evil planes were gaming us.

Witold addressed the driver. "My name is Witold, and this is my family." The farmer raised his hand in greeting and told us that his name was Leon.

Witold took out a wad of zlotys. "Mr. Leon, please take my family to Nowa Polana. This should be enough to cover your kindness towards us. I must stay here to look for petrol."

Leon happily pocketed the money and pulled on the horse's reins. "Yaaa, Mostek!"

As soon as we arrived, I knew that I loved this village! And

I loved Marysia's family, and they loved me more than they loved Wowka! Actually, they thought of him as a pest. "They" meant Marysia's parents, Zosia and Wojtek Podgurski, her two brothers, several aunts, uncles and cousins. I especially loved Tadek, Marysia's soon-to-be husband. He was so handsome, with brownish hair he kept pushing out of his eyes.

Our first village meal consisted of milk, cheese and sour cream, with freshly baked bread. Zosia surprised me with a small piece of red ribbon she tied around my right wrist. "To ward off the evil eye." This is what Jews and Poles share: fear of the evil eye.

Wowka looked peeved. "How about my red ribbon?"

Everyone laughed, but Wowka was serious.   "I mean, I'm also a child. Thirteen is not a grown-up. Why is no one worried that the evil eye may harm me?"

Wojtek, Marysia's father, put an end to the conversation. "We ran out of red ribbons."

We were in a sturdy wooden house much like Grandfather's, but with just one floor. A horse with the noble name of Stanislaw lived in the barn. Two cows and perhaps a dozen cackling chickens concluded the livestock. The grounds were a mixture of green grass and brown dust. When we arrived, the weather was already chilly, but the air was sweet, and the sun shone brightly.

The rains came toward the end of September, and the farm filled with mud. Marysia's father threw down wooden boards, on which we walked, balancing ourselves like circus acrobats. For me it was a game in which I could get dirty and not be punished. The mud squooshed underneath the boards, and when you walked to the very end, the board lifted behind you and sprayed extra mud, sometimes throwing you down into it.

71

Mother spent most of the time in the kitchen with Marysia and Zosia, preparing a variety of dishes made with cabbage, such as borscht, cabbage leaves stuffed with chicken gizzards, and the Polish delicacy bigos, which consists of cooked sauerkraut with pickled cow's or pig's intestines.

Tadek brought me a very clever Polish book, The Girl with the Wet Head, by the famous Polish writer Janusz Korczak.

"I don't see wet hair," I said, looking at the pictures.

Marysia laughed. "What this expression means is that our young lady is confused, as if her hair was wet."

I listened to the story and put the letters together, one by one. But I could not yet read a complete page.

"I read fluently at your age," my brother said with a grimace. Mother told him to keep quiet.

That night, Mother whispered in my ear, "Janusz Korczak is a Jewish doctor in Warsaw called Henryk Goldszmit." The information meant nothing to me.

One day, my father drove up with Mr. Witold, in an old car, not the limousine.

"Everything in Bialystok is wonderful, and everyone sends their love," Father and Witold said in unison, as if they had rehearsed it. We sat down to a hearty meal of beef and cabbage, washed down with fine local beer. Father took out a box of cigarettes, lit one and passed the box around.

Mother was aghast. "Kuba, you stopped smoking two years ago! So why start now?"

"I better tell you why I'm smoking again." He inhaled deeply.

"Poland has ceased to exist." Everyone stared at him in shock. "Remember how we were partitioned between 1795 and 1919?" Everyone nodded. "We have again been partitioned between Russia and Germany."

Marysia's father buried his face in his hands. "So now we have the Bolsheviks ruling over us?"

Father nodded. "Marysia and my family left Bialystok as citizens of the Polish Republic, but we return as Stalin's prisoners. The only good thing about this treaty between Hitler and Stalin is that it promises peace for the next ten years."

Together with Marysia, we returned to our apartment in Bialystok. Waiting for Father was an official letter from the new Soviet Governor of Bialystok, informing that the Wola factory had been confiscated by the Soviet Union. Mother's eyes glistened with tears. Father was deep in thought, recalling perhaps his last encounter with Stalin in Odessa.

"So it begins," was his only comment.

The following day, whether out of habit or pride, Father showed up at the factory, but was not allowed into his office. Installed there was a Commissar in a green military tunic, its front covered with medals like a breastplate. The medals clinked when the Commissar moved his torso. For a long time, Father sat on the bench outside his former office. Finally, the Commissar appeared before him and extended his hand. "Good morning, Yakov Markovich. I am Commissar Grigori Vasilyevich Tarpovski." They shook hands. "We know everything about you."

You know everything about everyone, Father whispered under his breath.

"You have an advanced degree in Marxist Economics from the University of Odessa. Very impressive. Please step into my office."

They went in. The Commissar sat down, his huge behind tormenting my father's armchair.

"You and I are men of the world, and therefore may, from time to time, change our fields of interest. For example, I was very good in what I did before." Father was afraid to inquire about the nature of the Commissar's previous career. "But I have been thrust here very swiftly, and I do not know much about dyeing textiles. So I am offering you the honorable position of bookkeeper and controller. We shall pay you a fine salary, trust me."

My father had no choice but to trust him.

November was proving to be an especially cold month, and the Rubinows were bankrupt. Everything we kept in the bank had been confiscated by the Soviet Union. My parents decided to keep Marysia, but the laundress and Miss Julie were let go. At first Miss Julie cried, then she comforted herself that she could travel to Warsaw and marry her fiancé, the penniless artist who still lived in a garret.

"Life may be better under the Germans than the Russians," Mother reflected.

Mother and Marysia did the cooking and cleaning. The floor in the salon lost its legendary shine.

"The proletariat does not deserve buffed floors," Mother said with rarely exhibited irony.

Shops and markets experienced food shortages, since a great

deal of it was making its way to the black market. The biggest help was Marysia's fiancé, Tadek, who drove his horse and buggy from the village, filled with fruit, vegetables and eggs.

Father prevailed on his new friend, the Commissar, to give Mother a job in the bookkeeping department. Anything to keep Comrade Rubinow happy, since Father was still running the factory, an excellent performance for which the Commissar took full credit.

On the next food delivery, Tadek and Marysia announced that they were getting married. We cried like babies. One by one, we were losing pieces of our lives.

Wowka saw it differently. "Shit, no more servants."

For the first time ever, all four Rubinows left the apartment each morning. Wowka marched off to the Hebrew Gymnasium, where cousin Bronek Kagan was also a student. Father locked the door and put the key into his breast pocket. Before dropping me off at Miss Applebaum's Nursery School, my parents had me repeat the following: "My name is Rachela Rubinow. I live on Zwirki Wigura Avenue, number 16, apartment 7, in Bialystok."

"Remember Rala, if you are lost, recite this to a policeman or a kind woman. Never a man!"

Once a week Father paid Miss Applebaum for my upkeep. The new Russian money came in large sheets, its red dye coloring one's hands. "These are rubles," Father explained, introducing me to the ugly money. "The larger the bills, the smaller their value."

My uncle Marek Rakowski, who had gained prominence as a survivor of Bereza Kartuska, returned to Bialystok from German-occupied Warsaw. He was alone. He sat down heavily and gulped some tea.

"I had to leave," he said with a sigh. "The Germans were arresting all Communists and socialists. Mary promised to leave with me, but at the last moment she changed her mind because she had patients booked for the month, and honor prevented her from running out on them." My parents looked at him with distress. "I shall go back in a month and bring her out."

Marek settled in Marysia's room. The Soviet authorities, impressed with his survival at Bereza Kartuska, rewarded him with a highly paid job as liaison between them and the Jewish community. It was an important task because of Bialystok's population of one hundred thousand, sixty percent were Jewish. Alas, Marek's big salary was paid in rubles, by now almost worthless. On the plus side, barter flourished, as doctors, cobblers or plumbers were thrilled to receive a chicken or a dozen eggs, instead of a stack of red paper money.

Even Marek, the devout Communist, admitted that having rubles would not fill one's belly. With the cunning of a veteran prisoner, he had his eyes open for anything he could bring home to make a meal. He brought flour, kasha, sardines, vegetables and bread. Long live the Bolshevik Revolution!

Unfortunately, sometimes Marek brought items one could not eat. For example, one evening he brought two large boxes. Guess what's inside?" he grinned from ear to ear. Unable to wait for us to guess, he blurted, "Christmas ornaments!"

"Christmas what?" Mother was amused.

The boxes were filled with shiny baubles, fragile and clanging, pink and mauve and blue, stars and horses, a carriage with a noble lady inside, and footmen on the dashboard. Marvel upon shining marvel, a pirate's treasure trove.

"Marek, explain something to me," Father drawled. "Why would the Soviets, who abolished Christmas, hand a treasure in ornaments to an atheist and his Jewish family?"

"You are right, but wrong. These are Polish capitalist ornaments, and the Soviets must get rid of them fast, because Christmas is around the corner, and they don't want their people to be tempted to put up a tree."

Mother interrupted, "And we will not put up a tree, either."

Marek was undaunted. "But Firochka, can't you see that these ornaments are art? Think of the imagination, the creativity. Jews are soulful people. We cannot destroy such beauty."

Father smiled. "You Rakowskis can talk each other into anything."

"I want a tree!" I cried, and started dancing around the beautiful things.

Wowka supported me. "Yes, the child's birthday is a few days after Christmas. So let Rala have a birthday tree."

What a wonderful idea! Everyone agreed that it was high time to make a fuss over me. Father and Wowka headed for the tree market, returning with a four-foot spruce. We decorated it lovingly and attached the St. Michael's star on top.

"Oh, beautiful!" I was thrilled. "Wait till Grandfather sees my tree."

Silence.

Marek was first to recover. "Ralinka, Grandfather should not be allowed into the house while the tree is here, and you must keep it a secret forever."

"Why?"

Wowka to the rescue! "Because Grandfather catches a disease when he comes in contact with green needles, the kind we have on this spruce. So keeping a secret is important."

Everyone nodded sagely. We promised to keep Grandfather out of the house till January 3, 1940, the day I turned four.

CHAPTER NINE

The first couple showed up on our doorstep in January, a week after my birthday. I looked at them in shock. The man was gripping what looked like a frozen suitcase. His hand was glued to it and seemed frozen. Their coats were covered with snow and icicles. The woman hugged herself, staring at the floor where her melting coat was dripping.

"Rabbi Jacob Meyer said that you would take us in," the man said in Yiddish through chattering teeth.

Mother ushered them in and closed the door. Father told them to undress completely and covered them with blankets. Mother warmed up milk and put cups into their hands.

"Is anything frozen?" Father asked.

"Possibly, probably." The man's hands shook as he attempted to hold on to the warm mug. The woman's mug fell to the floor, and she started to cry.

Fortunately, Uncle Marek walked in. He hugged the strangers. and in that moment the man took up crying.

"You know them?" Mother was curious.

"No, but I know of them," Marek said. The pair nodded. "They are bezhenzis, the Russian word for escapees from the German side of Poland. You see, according to our agreement with Hitler, no population is allowed to cross from one side to the other. Meaning, that if the NKVD finds them here, they'll be sent back to the Germans. More information later. Our first order of business is to call Cousin Sol to check them out."

"Oh, my God, no!" Mother cried. Solomon Shapira M.D., was the best surgeon in Bialystok.

Marek made the call, and half an hour later Cousin Sol rang the bell. He was a short man with a tie and suspenders but no jacket under his navy blue coat. His thin spectacles and a high thinker's forehead made him look creative. He did not hug or kiss the strangers, but addressed us with a curt, "Everyone out of the room."

"Hypothermia," was the diagnosis when he reemerged ten minutes later. "I must amputate. Her toes are useless, and he will lose his left leg below the knee. I do not want to know their names."

Mother looked closely at her cousin. "You look tired."

"This is just the beginning. These people will descend on us by the droves, and in worse shape than this pair." He ran his fingers through his receding hair. "Please set up Wowka's room for the procedure."

"Why my room?" Wowka was indignant.

"Shut your mouth!" Father hissed.

Later that evening, Cousin Sol operated on the strangers.

That night Uncle Marek and my parents relaxed, sipping cognac. Marek drank more than usual, and they didn't ask why.

"I'm going back to Warsaw," he said at last.

Mother looked scared. "You can't. You'll freeze like Mr. and Mrs. Freizinger." Sher had learned our guests' names.

"No, I have connections with my Communist brethren. Through them I get reports that the Germans are crowding the Jews into a ghetto surrounded by barbed wire and cutting their living space and food rations. This time, I must persuade Mary to leave."

Marek's connections enabled him to be driven to Warsaw and smuggled into the ghetto. He would later describe the squalor, the disease, the hunger. There was no doubt that these conditions would cause thousands of deaths. Dr. Mary Rakowski had set up her dental practice in the basement of a three-story building on Mila Street.

By the end of January, Marek was back—not frozen, but thin and depressed. "She refused to come," he reported dejectedly. "There are few dentists practicing in the ghetto and even fewer who have access morphine and penicillin. Her outside Aryan sources continue to supply it. She cannot abandon her patients."

The question lingered. Why hadn't Marek stayed with Mary to help her, but opted instead to save himself? Father insisted that Marek was selfish, and that his noble sermons about the common man were insincere. Mother reminded him that Marek had survived Bereza Kartuska, and perhaps it was enough suffering for one man, at least for a while. Besides, who can set himself up as judge in these terrible times?

At our next Sabbath meal, Grandfather explained that he had attached us to a city-wide network to take in as many refugees as we could. A call for surgeons had gone out from every rabbi and head of Jewish organizations. "You are not alone in this, almost all Jews are taking up the burden."

As predicted, more and more escapees came into the city. The forest they crossed was the densest and most primeval in Europe. The sick and frozen were the lucky ones.

No one knew how many had died in the crossing, because the people were leaderless and no one kept a tally.

Wowka's room had become a permanent operating room, and the salon was turned into a dormitory and hospital. Mostly a hospital, since hardly anyone emerged undamaged. There were no beds, and people slept on mattresses brought in by volunteers. I was moved into my parents' bedroom, and Wowka into my room. Uncle Marek was now in General Wola's quarters.

Dr. Sol recruited a few of his surgeon colleagues, causing the operating room to be busy day and night. Morphine bought on the black market was becoming scarce, and the groans and screams from the salon were loud, haunting the dreams both of the well and the suffering.

Grandfather had become a leader in this "Operation Save One Another." "This effort is a great achievement. Our part in this chain is to get the escapees on their feet and hand them over to other volunteers who will move them elsewhere. We don't want to know where. Secrecy is everything, and I warn you not to succumb to curiosity."

Before sending them away, our task was to transform the refugees into normal looking citizens. Jews everywhere collected clothing, to cover amputees with voluminous garments that would hide their deformities. One man, whom we knew only as Shlomo, was especially tall and broad. When his left leg was amputated, his body leaned sideways, sort of askew, and he needed an especially long coat. Mother remembered that Grandfather had been put in charge of Grandfather Rubinow's camel hair coat, over which Father and Uncle Ossya had fought and became estranged. Mother fetched the coat and gave it to Shlomo as a parting gift.

Father still left every morning for work, but Mother took a leave of absence, because it was unwise to allow the refugees the run of the house. One evening, as the sick coughed and spat blood, and Father had not yet returned from work, Wowka grabbed me by the hand and pulled me into what was once my room. "Ralka, what do you think happens to all those arms and legs that Cousin Sol cuts off?"

A lousy question. I was too scared to think about it. I must run away from my brother. On the other hand, what did happen to the arms and legs?

"Aha, I can see you're interested. Well, the first thing Cousin Sol does is put the fingers, arms, toes"—I was already crying— "into that huge white bucket we once used for laundry…"

"Stop! You are a liar!" I punched my brother in the chest. I should have run from him the moment he mentioned the limbs.

"I'm telling you the truth. Haven't you noticed that now Mama uses the grey bucket for laundry? Which means that the white bucket is used for arms and legs." I spat on his shoe and ran out of the room.

That night I dreamed that I was in a dark forest, the kind the refugees had walked through, and that I was chased by an army of cut-off legs gushing with blood. I woke up crying, but the sound was not loud enough for my parents to separate from the moans coming from the salon.

The next day Wowka repeated his offer. I stood there, thinking it over. Seeing my indecision, he grabbed me by the hand and led me down into the building's cellar, shrouded in nearly total darkness. "Here." he pointed to a distant wall. "See those buckets upon buckets of arms and legs, and small things like fingers and toes?"

The previous night's visions returned. I freed myself from his grasp and ran out of the cellar, crying. He ran after me, scooped me up in his arms and brought me upstairs.

"No," I told him when he set me down in my parents' bedroom. "You are a very bad brother, because you do mean things to me."

He laughed.

The refugee children taught me an interesting new game. We gathered every broomstick, rod, even Father's walking stick, and gave one to each child. Then we closed a door and stood in front of it banging and yelling, "Jude heraus! Jude heraus!" which meant in German, "Jew, come out." At first the adults let us play, but after less than an hour they decided to end it, saying, "Children, you are forbidden to play this game ever again."

But there were other games, and now I had children my own age to play with. For a while, Wowka stayed away from us. Then one day, he approached us with his authoritative height and said that he had a fantastic new game for us. "Little ones! Let me show you how you can smash something and pretend it's a German."

We whooped with delight.

Wowka ran into his/my bedroom and returned with his tennis racket and a container of balls. He marched us into my parents' bedroom, the one that at present also housed Uncle Marek, who had surrendered his room to refugees. Wowka positioned himself at a distance from Mother's beloved crystal chandelier. "This chandelier was manufactured in Bavaria, which is Germany, and it is time for us to smash this German monstrosity."

He closed his left eye and aimed a tennis ball at one of the twelve crystal sockets. Shards flew over the carpet. The children clapped their hands, but I was horrified. This was the most awful thing my brother had ever done.

"Wowka, stop it, stop right now!" I shouted and ran toward him. All I could do was hit his leg.

"Pay her no attention, he dragged me to the side. "She is a cry baby."

I ran out to fetch an adult who could stop Wowka from destroying the rest of the chandelier. All I found was an old lady whom I took with me to the bedroom. By now, half the sockets had been destroyed. Before we could intervene, Wowka tired of the game and went out for a walk in the park.

Our parents returned home droopy-eyed and haggard. At once they were confronted by the smashed chandelier and the glassy mist on the carpet. Mother cried helplessly, but she could not lie on the bedspread, because it was covered with glass.

"Kuba," she said, "it's one of the refugee children. How can they be so ungrateful? After all we've done for them."

Father, of course, knew better. He grabbed his belt and ran down the stairs. I believed that this time Wowka deserved a huge beating. After a while Father returned, dragging a limping Wowka. My brother's cheeks were so red that he must have endured several powerful slaps.

Father stared at him without pity. "I don't need a brilliant son. I need a human being."

In the spring the flow of refugees receded. We breathed happily as the apartment returned to its rightful owners. Still, Mother was curious why they stopped coming. She turned to Marek. "It's spring and mild. I should imagine it being the best time to get out of Warsaw."

A strange look passed between my father and Marek. My uncle said, "Things have changed. These days it is difficult to get out of Warsaw."

Mother had other things on her mind and did not pursue this inquiry. Now the five of us left the apartment in the morning, and my parents were able once more to lock their door. I had my mother back and was reunited with my dolls and stuffed animals. Late in the afternoon, my parents picked me up at Miss Applebaum's Nursery School, and we headed home. Every day we started our walk with me reciting: "My name is Rachela Rubinow and I live on…" They laughed and reassured me that it was only a game.

Soon after the refugees' departure, Uncle Marek brought us a surprise gift: a mammoth painting that we hung over the fireplace, then stepped back to admire. Staring at us were three huge fat cows. Brown with white spots, they were drinking water from a brook. I was fascinated with the cows and, looking closer, I noticed the cows' bellies expanding as they drank. And drank. These were thirsty cows! So, if the cows were drinking so much, why did the brook remain full?

Marek was thrilled with our reaction to his gift. The artist is my friend Alonso Levy, who was forced out of his apartment and is unable to find a place for his largest painting. So he decided to gift it to you in gratitude for all the dinners you fed him. I also thank you for feeding my other hungry friends."

It was getting warm enough to play outside. But not for me. I was stricken with the disgusting sickness of chicken pox. Wowka inspected the sores on my face, clucked his tongue and rendered a verdict. "Ralka, your disease is called leprosy, and you will die tomorrow."

What my brother was missing was that by now I was smarter than he. Clearly, if my brother predicted my death, I shall live for a million years. But I did look revolting and was nauseated. Due to my sickness, Mother stayed away from work and fed me lukewarm cream of wheat.

"Open wide," she implored. When I opened, I screamed, because my mouth was full of sores. From then on, Mother delicately wedged the spoon between my teeth.

Unexpectedly, one more refugee showed up. Grandfather had convinced my parents to shelter a young man who was very special to him. He was Joseph Kessenbaum, the nephew of Grandfather's good friend from his synagogue, Froyke Kessenbaum. Miraculously, Joseph had managed to escape from Warsaw and hide in the forest from Russian patrols. Once in Bialystok, he proceeded to his uncle's house, only to discover that they lived in close quarters not suitable for hiding. Grandfather sent him over to us.

Joseph was skinny like the other refugees. He was twenty-seven, not as young as we thought. Medium height, though compared to Father and Wowka he appeared short. Grandfather promised that soon he would find Joseph a permanent residence.

Recently, my parents had resumed their bridge games. I loved those gatherings, because for a few minutes I would become the center of attention. Inevitably, a player would ask me, "Rala, tell us, is there going to be war?"

I would cock my head and, relishing the moment, pronounce "yes" or "no," depending on my mood. When I said "no," they applauded, but my "yesses" were greeted with sighs. From then on my pronouncements were always an emphatic "no."

The next bridge game in our apartment took place two days after Joseph's arrival. The mood was exuberant, because I had just shouted an enthusiastic "No!" to war. Another pleasant surprise was that Joseph turned out to be an avid bridge player, which made Mother exclaim, "You can live with us forever!"

While this was going on, we did not realize that someone was knocking on the door. As the knocks intensified, the card players paused.

A voice outside shouted in Russian, "Open in the name of Generalissimo Joseph Stalin!"

Mother whispered to Joseph to climb under the intricate ruffles covering my bed.

At the door stood everyone's enemy, the NKVD. Mother ran to the door and greeted the agents with a polite Russian welcome. There were four men dressed in black leather coats. Three of the coats were of cheap leather, but the fourth claimed good quality and style, so we knew who was the leader.

The Good Coat introduced himself as Commissar Major Yevgeny Rosstovsky. "I received a report that you are harboring a fugitive." He scanned the room, focusing on the bridge players. Asked for identification, everyone presented the correct documents.

"Card players," he hissed. "So bourgeois." The Cheap Coats snickered.

From the salon he entered into the bedroom, where he found me sitting in bed, ghastly sores covering my face and hands.

Mother explained, "We have her in the bedroom and not the salon because she's contagious."

I was about to say that I have leprosy, but Rosstovsky quickly stepped away from me and my sores. He wished us good luck with our capitalist pastime and departed.

That night Joseph was moved to a safer location.

CHAPTER TEN

I t appeared that the NKVD could not stay away from us. Two weeks after their first visit, we heard once more the major's familiar voice from the hallway. "Open in the name of Generalissimo Joseph Vissariyonovich Stalin!"

"Oh, shit," Father said in Russian. Defiantly, he waited thirty seconds before opening the door.

And there he was, Major Rosstovsky in his expensive leather coat and his three minions in cheap clothing. "Good evening, Comrade Yakov Markovich. Please go back to your supper; we shall not stay long." Considering this an order, Father sat down, but instead of eating we stared at the intruders.

The three subordinates produced a tape measure with which they circled around us at the dinner table. Seeing that we were scared enough, they confidently measured every room, including the kitchen and bathroom. Each time they completed a section, they jotted down something in a notebook. When the measuring was completed, they conferred, shaking their heads in dismay.

Rosstovsky addressed my father. "Comrade Rubinow,

according to the laws of the Soviet Socialist Republics, your family of four occupies the living space of eighteen Soviet citizens. Congratulations!" They laughed.

Without another word, the foursome turned around and left.

Ten days later, Major Rosstovsky and his family appeared on our doorstep. All eight Rosstovskys, laden with bundles and sweating profusely. September had always been the hottest month in Bialystok and this one, in 1940, was no exception. There was the major's wife, Olga, a plump bleached blonde desperately needing a fresh application of peroxide; four Rosstovsky children ranging in age from a baby to a boy of seven or eight; Rosstovsky's father, a former NKVD agent, and lastly his wife, Sofia, a frail woman with large watery eyes.

The major led his family on a tour of our apartment. "Here, Papa, is the salon where we shall spend the evenings listening to radio and invite friends to come over and play the piano."

He turned to us. "Do any of you bourgeois play the piano?" We shook our heads. "Don't tell me you could not afford lessons."

The old lady, Sofia, not a curious soul, sat down with us at the table and withdrew her knitting, paying us no attention. Rosstovsky's voice kept on loud and clear. "The Rubinows will have their bedroom and the little room where the dolls are. The rest of the apartment belongs to the warriors of the Soviet Union. Do you agree, Yakov Markovich?"

Father only stared. A tiny victory. The old lady did not interrupt her knitting, the needles hissing against each other like insects.

Back at the table, the major withdrew a piece of paper from his coat pocket and continued to rub it in. "So you see, Comrades

Rubinow and Rubinowa, we have left you a very generous living space. You will have access to the kitchen for fifteen minutes in the morning, and thirty minutes to prepare supper. But you cannot eat your meals in the kitchen. It will be too crowded. Olga will hand out a sheet showing how long each of you is allowed to stay in the bathroom."

"Jews are known to spend too much time in their bathrooms," chimed in Old Rosstovsky.

Wowka's eyes raged. He loved to read in the bathroom. He must have read all of Alexander Dumas on the toilet. No more!

The Rosstovskys made themselves comfortable in our house, and we took it as a sign to return to the bedroom.

Before we did, Olga said, "The food here is yours. We shall not eat it. We are supplied with food by the NKVD."

Later, the telephone rang, but we could not answer because the Rosstovskys had taken away our phone privileges. Olga spoke to someone, then hung up and related this message.

"Marek Yakovlevich called to say hello."

Uncle Marek did not return to the apartment.

Each morning, the four Rubinows happily left the apartment and went about our daily activities, my parents to the Wola factory, Wowka to the Hebrew high school and I to Miss Applebaum's Nursery School. We often reunited at the nursery school and proceed to Kupiecka Street for supper with Grandfather, where Fanya and her family now lived because the Soviets had confiscated their apartment. The mood became jolly whenever Uncle Marek joined us.

"So where do you live now?" Father asked him.

Grandfather had his answer. "He lives with some starving musicians and painters."

"I was invited to stay with the NKVD in their barracks," Marek chuckled, "but I respectfully declined."

Soon the People's Commissariat for Military Affairs, the NKVDE, closed down Miss Applebaum's Nursery School, labeling her "a capitalist who exploits the proletariat." What to do with Rala? The solution came from an unexpected quarter. Olga Rosstovsky offered to watch me together with her children.

My inclusion was normal, because I spoke Russian. Having no dolls or toys of their own, they appropriated everything I owned. Their Russian books were shabby and contained boring stories about children driving tractors, gathering hay in the field, or singing in a choir. All the children in the pictures were dressed alike: white blouses and red ties. My grandmother Jadwiga would have wept seeing such fashion abuse.

I barely noticed that at home we had switched to Yiddish, a language the Christians do not understand. Mother advised me, "Don't talk too much when you are with them. Remember, they are not our family or our friends. And never recite Pushkin, because they will punish you for being too smart. In fact, with them, you should speak as little as possible. Be sweet, smile, and always say 'thank you' and 'please.' Say you promise."

"Yes, I promise."

"On your word of honor?"

"Yes! Yes on my word of honor!"

Not speaking much meant being totally bored. I missed my

friends from nursery school. So many toys, and Miss Applebaum and her sister's telling intelligent stories about flying angels and ships sailing in mysterious oceans.

My current pleasure was visiting with my three cows in the salon. The painting was mine. No matter what the Rosstovskys thought they owned, this painting would never be theirs.

The cows were still drinking water from the endless brook.

"You cows have a better life than me," I told them. "You are in the middle of green trees and flowers, and you three seem to be good friends. Sometimes I think you may dance the polka. Thank you, great artist Alonso Levy, for gifting me your painting!"

The old NKVD man loved to rummage through my parents' belongings. He waited till they left and then plunged into their dresser. He would take out the neatly folded contents of each drawer, shirts, shorts, brasseries, shake them out energetically, and replace them in the drawer in a heap. As I watched him each day, I noticed that he stole nothing. This meant that he was as bored as I, but instead of watching cows, he rummaged through underwear.

But one day, he found something he wanted. It was Grandfather Mark Rubinow's round gold pocket watch, with a thick gold chain attached to it. "Aha!" he bellowed happily. "Look Sofia, an onion!"

His grandchildren surrounded him, jumping up and down. I felt an urge to speak. "It's not an onion. It's my grandfather's watch."

"Oh, no, Ralichka. It is now Sergei's grandfather's watch." Sergei was five and allowed to touch this onion.

"Yes, I know you wonder about the name," the Russian

continued. "Because this watch is so round and smooth, it reminds us of onions."

I wanted to say that real onions do not tick, but I remembered Mother's instructions and kept quiet.

Energized by his discovery, the old man shook out every drawer throughout the house. He was thoroughly frustrated when he found nothing more. One evening he confronted Father.

"Yakov Markovich, I demand to see your onions."

Father explained that these watches were old-fashioned and that young men no longer wore them. But Rosstovsky was unshaken. "Son, it is well known that you Jews have jewelry stashed away."

Sensing a menace, Mother went over to Grandfather's house and coaxed him to give up his favorite gold watch. He put up no resistance. "I had business with Russians of every generation, so you better give him what he demands."

Now the retired NKVD man possessed enough onions to satisfy his lust. He displayed both watches on his chest next to the medals he had earned for a lifetime of dispensing cruelty.

Since Olga and her mother-in-law had taken over the kitchen, my parents and Wowka no longer ate breakfast at home. Mother washed me and helped me dress, then deposited me in front of the kitchen, where I joined her children for a breakfast of diluted cream of wheat and a glass of milk. Luckily, Olga never asked my parents to pay her for my breakfast and lunch.

When winter turned the avenue and the park into a sparkling white fairytale, I turned five. We went to Grandfather's house and celebrated with a hearty dinner of roasted chicken and fried potatoes. I missed Rala's birthday tree and the shining ornaments that Uncle Marek had been given by the godless Bolsheviks.

Our faces were grim as Grandfather delivered a small sermon. "What made us Jews survive for two thousand years despite persecutions, pogroms and poverty is our faith in God. Also telling jokes." We looked at him seated at the head of the table, grinning. "So, does anyone have a good joke?"

Father had a good excuse. "Father-in-law, you know I can't tell jokes."

"Anyone for a joke, except Yakov?"

Wowka stood up and told a Russian joke that made Grandfather reprimand him in a harsh voice. "You are too young to tell dirty jokes." he thundered. I wish I understood what the joke meant.

"Where did you learn such filth?" Mother asked.

"Old Commissar Rosstovsky told it to me in secret."

There were no more jokes that evening.

We had a visitor! My favorite person, Marysia, came to see us. The time was between my birthday on January 3 and Woka's on February 11, when he would turn fifteen. Marysia and her husband Tadek came up from the village in a horse and buggy. He must have ridden carefully, because Marysia was pregnant, a condition Mother referred to as "delicate with child" They arrived late in the day when we were at home. Mother introduced Marysia to the Rosstovskys as her niece. How could you tell the NKVD that you had employed a maid?

Mother whisked the visitors into our bedroom, where we kissed and hugged and slobbered over each other. Marysia brought me a sweater she had knitted. I cried because it was my first new piece of clothing in a year.

"Happy birthday, Ralusia! You are such a big girl."

There was also a bag of my favorite sugar cookies, a container of fresh sour cream—I love sour cream!—six hard-boiled eggs and a freshly baked loaf of bread. She also brought me a lovely soft rag doll that I immediately named "Marysia."

I whispered, "The Moskals took my dolls." Moskal is a bad name that Poles call the Russians.

Tadek took over. "It is a grave family matter that we come to discuss with you. We would like to take Rala with us to the farm. It's better for the child to be away from all this." He pointed beyond the door.

My heart was pounding. For the first time, my fate was being decided in front of me. Father was deep in thought. Mother looked stunned. My parents exchanged a look of understanding. Mother cried, and Father spoke.

"Thank you, Marysia and Tadek. And thank your parents for their kindness. But whatever happens, we must remain together."

Back to my boring life. Besides communicating with the cows, I would sit alone on the windowsill and dream about what the adults called "the good old days." I looked across at the park and imagined strolling there with Miss Julie.

Passover came in April, and Wowka received eight days of recess from the Hebrew gymnasium. When the students returned after the holiday, they found the doors locked and a notice in Russian saying, "This school has been closed by order of

Generalissimo Joseph Stalin. The students are advised to report to the school on Branicki Street, where they will be instructed in Russian language and history."

Now, Wowka was also cut off from learning. Mother took me every morning to Grandfather's house, where we later gathered for dinner. Wowka and cousin Bronek, Fanya's and Grisha's son, would often disappear, but returned for dinner.

Nothing was real. It was like flying in the air without wings— and bound to crash to earth.

PART TWO:

SUNFLOWER IN THE SNOW

CHAPTER ELEVEN

People begin this kind of story with: "It was a night like any other." But, of course, it wasn't. Because on this night, two hours into June 22, 1941, the People's Commissariat for Military Affairs came for us. I was five, and my brother fifteen. The third knock was accompanied by Rosstovsky's official bark. "Open in the name of Generalissimo Josef Stalin!"

Father opened our bedroom door. And there he stood, resplendent in his uniform, his medals like circles cut out of an aluminum pot. Gloating. His three police underlings kept their hands on holstered pistols. Behind them, the Rosstovsky family gathered to watch.

I was confused. "Why do you dress up to come from your room to ours?"

Silence. Rosstovsky cleared his throat. He took a paper out of his pocket and read, "By order of the Supreme Soviet of Soviet Socialist Republics, you are repatriated to Eastern Provinces. You have twenty minutes to get ready and are allowed only as much luggage as each of you can carry."

We stared at each other with fear and confusion. Father was first to come to his senses. He rapidly spoke to Mother in Yiddish. "First, the jewelry. Where we are going, we can live for a year or more by selling your jewelry. Also, your pretty lingerie, nightgowns and robes, especially the ones with lace." Mother looked stunned, as Father continued, "I'll go up to the attic and bring down the cloth samples." Those were rolls of fabric gifted to Father by manufacturers for his perfect dye jobs.

Father's instructions were stern and rapid. "Everyone must wear as much clothing as we can. Especially winter clothes. Coats, hats, boots, mufflers. And hurry!"

"We are going on a trip!" I announced with glee, jumping on one foot.

"Shut up, you idiot!" Wowka hissed, packing his rucksack.

Rosstovsky did not interfere as my parents threw our belongings into a large suitcase. I was given a satchel for my dolls, and Wowka was ordered to carry it together with his own rucksack.

I wore my beaver-lined coat and boots forced over three pairs of wool socks, as if I were going ice-skating in June. Hardly breathing under the mass of clothes, I yelled to my brother, "Don't forget to put my rag doll Marysia into the satchel."

"Everyone out and march downstairs!" shouted Rosstovsky, keen to be done with this. As we filed out of our apartment, none of them looked us in the eye. Flanked by Rosstovsky and his leather coats, we were herded down the stairs in the darkness and stifling heat of a summer night.

Downstairs stood a truck covered with green canvas, in it other people with suitcases and bundles. A large crowd had gathered outside, some of them holding hands with those in the truck. Many on the truck and in the street wept and prayed in Polish and Yiddish.

Armed NKVD agents pushed families assembled on the street away from the truck, causing those holding hands to separate. The NKVD loosened the truck's hinges to let us in. A policeman lifted me aboard, and my parents followed. Wowka climbed in last, and the NKVD secured the hinges.

"Oh my God! Where are they taking us?" people lamented.

I remained upfront, staring at the street below and sweating profusely under my winter clothes. By now I understood that something awful was happening to us, and it terrified me. Mother hugged herself to stop shaking.

Suddenly the street lights came on, and everyone's face sprang into focus, encased in a frame of silver glow. Two Soviet agents jumped into the truck. Slowly we began to move.

At this moment Aunt Fanya appeared, running toward the moving truck.

"Aunt Fanya!" I screamed at the top of my lungs.

She ran as fast as she could, her hair loose behind her back, her breasts shaking up and down. She was waving her arms and shouting, "Firochka!"

Panting, Fanya reached the truck at last. Mother opened her satchel, withdrew her jewelry box and shouted to my aunt, "Fanya, catch!" As the box traveled through the air, Father lurched to grab his wife's arm, but it was too late, because it had already landed in Fanya's arms. As Father glowered over her, Mother yelled to her sister in a piercing shriek, "We won't need this where we're going."

Father's face darkened with rage, "Fira, what the hell did you do?"

"What do I need jewelry when we all know that the Russians are taking us to the forest to kill us!"

People who overheard her uttered a giant scream. The Soviet agents did nothing to stop the shrieks, as if panic made their job easier. On the truck was a nobleman, Count Henryk Stankiewicz, owner of rich estates in the county of Podlasie. The Count grabbed Father's sleeve.

"Will you please control your wife before everyone goes mad?"

"Stop being hysterical!" Father snapped at his wife. But she sobbed even louder, and he slapped her across the face.

"Only a Jew would hit a woman in public," was Count Stankiewicz's haughty reaction.

To spite him, Father answered the nobleman in Russian. "Dear Comrade Stankiewicz, perhaps you haven't noticed that many titled Polish men disappeared two years ago into the darkest hole of history."

Dawn was breaking when the truck pulled into the Bialystok Railroad Station, already bursting with activity. Other trucks filled with people like us kept arriving from all over the city, from Christian and Jewish neighborhoods alike.

People were ordered out of the trucks, only to form mobs on the platform. The NKVD had not yet released the hinges of our truck, so we were stuck there, a sliver of humanity pushing against each other in a limited space. Looking down, I experienced a terrible fear: I might get lost in this monstrous crowd! If I don't hang on to Mother and Father every second of the way, I'll be lost and die somewhere all alone. Then Father took me in his arms, and I felt safe.

Before us stood a train. It was so long, it seemed to snake into infinity.

"An echelon," Father whispered. "That's a police train carrying people from their homes to an unknown destination." The word "destination" meant that they would not kill us, because we were headed somewhere.

As we jumped onto the platform, we heard a familiar voice. "Hello, let me through; I'm looking for Esther and Yakov Rubinow!" It was my uncle Marek Rakowski, bellowing at the NKVD.

"Here, here!" cried Father and Wowka, visible above everyone's heads. Marek's appearance was the ultimate confirmation that we would not be killed.

Marek spoke fast. "I am leaving with a Red Army transport," he said anxiously. "I was unable to make contact with Mary in Warsaw."

"Why are you leaving now?"

"Because it's time."

The NKVD were filling up each railroad car to capacity and sealing the doors before moving on to the next car. Mother's eyes were still following her brother's disappearing silhouette, when the order came for us to get into the next car.

People from several trucks were prodded into each car. The young and strong pushed and shoved to get ahead and seize a good space on the floor. An older man, clearly a prankster, found himself an easy foil.

"Noble Count Stankiewicz, did you know that the Soviets are shipping all of us to a Jewish State they've set up in Crimea? So, you better learn Yiddish!" The man laughed at his own joke, but no response came from the Count.

Dawn shone brightly as the last cars were bolted.

CHAPTER TWELVE

Ours were not cattle cars, because they had never transported livestock. The blackness inside confirmed that these cars had recently unloaded a shipment of coal, and that the police didn't bother to hose them down before stuffing in human cargo. The floors, walls and ceiling were covered with flying soot, velvety things detaching themselves from the walls like shapeless spiders. In minutes, people began to cough, and those with breathing problems were in for a gruesome ordeal.

"It's like Dante's Inferno," Mother groaned. The Count raised his eyebrows.

We were soon transformed into a huddle of blackened bodies attempting to arrange ourselves atop our luggage, the train's wheels beneath us rattling with satanic speed. We would soon find out why the conductor was in such a rush.

"Kuba, are we going to suffocate?" Mother asked.

"No. But some older people may die."

Relief came at our first stop, when the NKVD opened the

shafts near the ceiling. Outside was pleasant and mild, the perfect weather for a bicycle ride. Dazzling rays of sunshine peeking through the shafts were turning our black walls into an orange hell.

Everyone was hungry, but I was starving. Most people had packed some food. Not so Count Stankiewicz, who had found himself a companion from his own social class, Countess Bronislawa Dolinka. Neither of them had brought food.

"They will feed on manna from heaven," Father said derisively. We had a loaf of bread and two covered cups, one with butter, the other with jam. The butter had melted. Father had also carried a bottle of water and a package of Russian vanilla crackers he had brought from the office. A good haul.

Suddenly a loud voice spoke in Yiddish from the car's depth. "We must share our food."

The voice belonged to Rabbi Eli Sherov, head of the Agudas Yisroel Synagogue. The rabbi was of medium height with an authoritarian grey beard. I thought he was ancient, but he was probably just very old. Next to him was his son Yossi, also a rabbi.

The two rabbis walked around collecting food into a pillowcase. Some resisted, too frightened to let go of what they thought might be their last crumbs for a long time.

"These men were taken without their wives," Father observed. "The NKVD snatched anyone they found at home. Thank God we are together."

Count Stankiewicz surprised us with a ham sandwich he produced out of the pocket of his voluminous raincoat. In went the sandwich into the pillowcase. Somehow, the resourceful rabbi maneuvered the sandwich into a solitary corner, to separate it from the kosher food.

The rabbi selected hard-boiled eggs and fruit for the children. The adults ate bread dipped in melted butter with a sip of water. The ham sandwich ended up with a Christian family, a professor of anthropology at Bialystok University, and his wife, a poet.

Wowka winked at me. "The rabbi poisoned your apple, like Snow White's evil stepmother. Let me taste it to make sure."

I rolled away and out of his reach, where I greedily finished my apple. Wowka opened his rucksack and removed a pile of books from the Bialystok Public Library. He showed me the return date on one of them: July 2, 1941.

"Ha ha," he said. "I have so much time. It's only June 22."

Since Wowka unpacked his books, I asked for my dolls. He blinked, and I became suspicious. "You were told to bring my toys in the other satchel. "

He hit his forehead with the palm of his hand. "I am really sorry, Ralka, but I forgot the satchel back home."

I stopped breathing as I realized the finality of his act. At that moment I knew that I would never have another toy. With a rage I had never felt before, I flew at my brother and grabbed him by his hair. I pulled and pulled, taking advantage of his surprise. "You miserable dog!" I screamed. "You are worse than the dead arms and legs in our cellar. You are worse than Hitler! I hate you! I shall never ever forgive you!"

Wowka pushed me away. If anyone believed that this fight was over, they were wrong. Father took over from me and began choking his son. The people in the car looked on, a stunned audience. All one could hear were Wowka's gasps and Father's Russian curses. "Monster. Bloodsucker. Criminal…"

Reb Eli intervened, ordering Father to stop. As with Grandfather Jacob Meyer, Father obeyed. People looked away, hoping it was over.

They were wrong, because at this moment Mother threw herself on a bundle, face down, sobbing, "What a public disgrace! The Rakowskis never had such a vulgar display of bad manners." I crawled over to comfort her, but she pushed me away. "It's all your fault, Rala! "

"It's not my fault!" I replied, letting go of her. "It's Wowka's fault, because he hates me, and that's why he forgot my dolls!"

"You should not attack your brother over some stupid toys. I promise that as soon as we return home, I'll buy you all the toys you want. But first you must apologize to Wowka for pulling his hair."

"No! Never!"

"Then I shall never forgive you for being so obstinate."

Never forgive me? My mother had never said anything like this to me before.

We were submerged in darkness, weak rays of the setting sun peeking through the slats. People's faces receded from view, their bodies tired and motionless on their bundles.

I was alert and indignant. I am the smallest member of our family, so why do they blame me for everything? It isn't fair! I touched Mother's sleeve. "Mama, I love you, and I am terribly sorry that you're unhappy."

But that wasn't what she wanted. "I don't need your apology. It's your brother you apologize to."

I was furious. "Mama, if you don't say you'll forgive me even if I don't ask Wowka's forgiveness, I shall never go to sleep."

That night the legend of Rala Rubinow was born. It appears that I remained on my feet for an hour or more. Some people couldn't fall asleep, seeing a child leaning against a suitcase in an attempt to stay awake.

A man next to us woke up Father and pointed to me. He grabbed Mother, also awake, and said in a commanding voice, "Fira, tell Rala immediately that you forgive her."

I think she was relieved to have this mess come to an end. As soon as she said, "Rala, I forgive you," I fell on a pillow and into the deepest sleep.

Abruptly, the train stopped. Our car jerked and everyone woke up, disoriented. We climbed on our suitcases and peered through the slats. Dawn was breaking leisurely over a ramshackle hut.

"Must be the train station," Father said. "See the cardboard with the words Krassnaya Polyana, which in Russian means the Red Field."

As our conductor was refueling, the car doors opened wide enough for station workers to replace the buckets of urine and feces that had accumulated since we left home.

We were forbidden to step outside. "Water! We're dying of thirst!" people yelled into the void outside.

"The only water we have is green from a frog lake," said a station worker.

"Frogs were one of the better Egyptian plagues," Reb Eli said, smiling at the stranger. "We'll be grateful if you bring us some."

113

As the train took off, we sat in the car, happily sipping green water. Off again, the train tore into Russia's countryside at record speed.

Reb Eli sidled up to my father. "Yakov, you know the Russians better than anyone. What do you think the NKVD has in store for us?"

"First, honorable rabbi, rest assured that they will not kill us. But it worries me that the conductor is in such a hurry, as if escaping from something."

Then a very old lady fainted. When she was revived, Reb Eli asked her, "Mrs. Becker, why are you alone?"

"My sons knew that the police would come for them," she said, "because they are Zionist Revisionists. They went into the forest to hide, assuring me that the Soviets would have no interest in me." She laughed so hard that we thought she might faint again.

"My grandfather is a Zionist," I said. "But what's a Revisionist?"

"A Zionist in a hurry," explained Reb Eli. "Thank God, Mrs. Becker, at least your sons are safe."

The gnawing in our stomachs shouted food! But the train kept gaining speed, and once more the people looked desperate. I walked through the car hoping to find a girl with toys. I did find two boys, Pinny and Zac. "Oops!" I exclaimed. "You two look exactly like each other."

"Have you never seen identical twins?" one of them asked with a smirk. I sat down on their bundle, and they regaled me with stories of the pranks they had pulled on unsuspecting adults. These were such great stories that I forgot that I had come looking for dolls.

The train stopped. Ah, food! Father was the first to look through the slats, since he did not need a suitcase to stand on. Turning back, he reported in a jittery voice, "Russian soldiers are fighting over our train."

Whoever could, climbed up and peered outside. Wowka put me on his shoulders. "Ralka, watch history in the making."

The platform was filled with agitated Red Army soldiers.

"Where are their officers?" Father whispered.

The terrified soldiers were firing bullets in the air. In shock, we watched as our NKVD shot a Russian soldier trying to climb aboard. The train jerked into motion. The soldiers hanging onto it fell to the tracks. Once more we were on our way, hungrier than ever.

When the sun reached its peak, the train stopped.

"Will someone bring us food?" people cried.

"We didn't stop for food, but for coal," Father said grimly.

At this Wowka let out a belly laugh, and the Count said, "The English have a saying, something about coal and Newcastle, but I don't know if it's a joke."

Outside, two horse-driven carts carrying coal materialized from somewhere. The NKVD surrounded it like a cloud of locusts. More carts arrived with buckets of fresh water. Food!

"Ask the townspeople for food," advised the NKVD.

As if hearing our pleas, townspeople poured into the station.

"They know who we are," Father said, "they've seen people like us for a hundred years."

The peasants brought food. We grabbed whatever dishes we

had and stood at the open door, begging them to throw anything they could into our containers. There was bread, sometimes with butter, hard-boiled eggs, chunks of cheese, tomatoes, cucumbers, an onion…

"Damn," Wowka snorted. "We have been reduced to begging for food."

"Don't complain," Reb Eli rebuked him. "The Lord often disguises himself as a beggar."

"God have mercy on you poor souls," said the woman who dropped a piece of boiled chicken into Mother's outstretched Chinese bowl. She crossed herself. "We'll pray for you."

The train pulled away at maximum speed, as darkness descended once more.

"The conductor wants to run out the Army," Father explained, which did not reassure anyone.

Suddenly, a piercing noise emerged from the pillar of darkness, followed by flickering lights. The train was forced to a halt. Father looked through the slats. "It's Minsk. I suggest we don't look out, because terrible things are happening outside."

A flurry of shots. Disregarding Father's advice people climbed to watch.

"Russian soldiers seized a train," someone shouted. "They're throwing the people and their luggage to the platform and climbing aboard. The Minsk NKVD are escaping with the soldiers."

Would they attack us too? All around us people clutched each other, too frightened to breathe. More gunfire, followed by screams.

Again, Father warned, "Don't let the children see this!"

Wowka hoisted me on his back, and we climbed up. Now I saw everything. People who looked exactly like us, with children and bundles, screamed and cursed the soldiers who had evicted them.

Our train tore out of the station. My last image was of a girl my age, also with pigtails, sitting alone on the platform, sobbing. I remembered how terrified I still was that my parents might lose me. My parents saved me, but what happened to this girl's parents?

Silently, I cried. Out there in the darkness, all alone, was another Rala.

After riding for a long time in darkness, we heard a boom, then another, even stronger.

"Thunder," Mother said.

"No, Fira. Bombs. The world is at war."

The darkness grew menacing. No one slept. Our little corner of the world was punctured by regular bomb blasts, creating a feeling that we were riding toward the bombardment rather than leaving it behind.

CHAPTER THIRTEEN

"I am Commissar Andrei Ilyich Pamuzov of the NKVD," bellowed the little man in front of the camp barracks. "This will be your home until the government in Moscow makes up its mind what to do with you."

It was two weeks since our train had pulled out of the Bialystok Railroad station. Now we were off the train, somewhere in Siberia. It was the beginning of July and frightfully hot. After fourteen days and nights of nearly total darkness, we blinked from the onslaught of sunshine in a land famous for snow. We humans felt small, standing on an expansive terrain of flatland surrounded by shadowy mountain peaks. From where we stood, mountains were not mere shadows, but silhouettes floating in the sky as if unattached to the ground.

Back to Pamuzov: "Citizens of the former Polish state, you should be grateful to be under the protection of the Union of Soviet Socialist Republics!" He stopped, as if waiting for applause. When none came, he cleared his throat and continued. "We shall give you interesting work and plenty of food."

He was dressed in fine black leather, a costume we had become accustomed to seeing on our tormentors. But in this heat? Blinking in the sun, he paused for inspiration. Father shouted into the temporary silence, "What is this place called, Comrade Commissar?"

"Old Mud. The best lager in Siberia."

"The word lager, meaning concentration camp, is the same in Russian and German," the Bialystok University professor whispered.

Pamuzov lingered, as if at a loss for words. Then he clicked his heels and shouted, "Our goal is righteous! We shall be victorious!" He swept out of the barrack like a ballerina off a stage, followed by the two agents who usually accompanied a Commissar.

"So, what now?" Old Mrs. Becker expressed everyone's feelings.

All around, hungry people sat on their metal beds in frustration and fear. Wowka's face registered the terror of a caged animal. Mother and Father were holding hands, something I had not seen them do for a long time.

The sun had parched the mud for which this camp was named. The earth was cracked, forming dried squares sprouting yellow weeds. How could we settle into this life? Our barrack was filthy, the floor covered with a layer of dust blown in through shattered windows. Walls bore graffiti chiseled with knives that read: "Anastas Grigoryevich lived here and probably died. March, 1938." "Natasha's big brother says hello. April, 1939." Comparing these notes of yesteryear, we realized that nothing had been written since Natasha's brother had said hello, which meant that no one had lived here for two-and-a-half years. The desolation was proof enough.

One of the children found a well, so we grabbed our dishes and ran. Vigorous pumping brought up fistfuls of liquid mud. Count Stankiewicz strolled over. "Keep pumping everyone. With time, the water will clear. I have three wells on my estate, so I know what I'm speaking of."

"Nu, so he has an estate. Mazel tov," said a woman in a white blouse stained with sweat. Indeed, soon the water cleared, but Doctor Klein, who had come with us, said that we should drink but a few sips. "We have no idea what kind of soil this is," he explained. We filled up our dishes and returned to the barrack.

"This reminds me of a joke," said Mr. Weinberg, a stout man with a red nose. We needed a joke so much that everyone laughed even before Weinberg began.

The Count was displeased. "Weinberg, this is no time for jokes."

Reb Eli laughed more heartily than ever. "Trust me, Mr. Count. It is a prisoner's right, even duty, to tell jokes."

Mr. Wineberg brightened. "Rabinovitch and Mendelevitch are sailing on a ship during a storm. 'So how do you feel?' Rabinovitch asks Menedelevitch. 'Like in the Soviet Union. Endless space, I'm nauseous, and there's nowhere to run.'"

Everyone laughed more than the joke deserved.

"I'll never understand you, Jews," said the Count, with a resignation that might have been construed as sympathy.

"You may not believe this, Mr. Weinberg," beamed Reb Eli, "but I am a great admirer of Robinson Crusoe."

A truck on the horizon. Thank God, it's the NKVD!

"If they bring food, I shall kiss you Mr. Count," Reb Eli said joyfully.

The truck stopped. Carbine-toting policemen jumped off, pulling a water cistern. We lined up to drink real water. Our collective ahhh of pleasure was so sincere, it must have climbed up the mountaintop.

The NKVD also brought mattresses and what might have been sheets. The mattresses were stained and disgusting. Maybe they had been Anton's, of the wall graffiti. There was one sheet, a blanket and a pillow per person.

And yes—food arrived! Bread, cheese and milk. "Tomorrow will be a hot supper," a compassionate policeman comforted us. "Soviet word of honor."

The Count's face registered the contempt the Poles felt for a Russian's word of honor.

At night, Father and Wowka discovered that the beds were too short for them, leaving their feet dangling in air.

"Goddamned Bolsheviks," Wowka hissed.

"If you don't shut your mouth these Bolsheviks will come and chop off your feet," Father responded.

A few days later, it became clear what "meaningful employment" meant. In the vicinity of Old Mud was a rock quarry, last worked when the camp was operational. At this point the quarry was abandoned and useless, as if waiting for the Bialystok deportees to revive it. Each morning, the truck took our parents to the quarry, where they smashed rocks and stacked them into piles.

"So why don't they come to remove the rocks?" Count

Stankiewicz asked angrily, examining his blistered hands.

"Because, Comrade Stankiewicz," Father intoned, "all the Bolsheviks want is to keep us busy. They don't need rocks, because they don't build anything."

"Rubinow, you shouldn't speak recklessly about the government," interjected Mr. Weinberg, the one who had been telling jokes about Rabinovich.

Reb Eli cackled: "So what can they do to him? Send him to a prison camp in Siberia?"

"Now this is funny," the Count admitted grudgingly.

The guards wanted to take Wowka to the quarry, seeing as he was the tallest deportee, but Mother was determined to prevent it. Among us was Mr. Mosher, before the war the most accomplished forger in Bialystok, who at a price to be collected after the war, calligraphed for my brother a birth certificate that put his age at thirteen, too young to work. The guards raised their eyebrows, but let it go.

While the adults worked, Wowka gathered around him the children left in the camp and told us stories from the many books he had read. "There was a captain called Nemo, who built a giant submarine..." We were enthralled. Or: "Once upon a time in the land of France rode heroes who called themselves the Three Musketeers, and who picked up another musketeer on their way to meet the Queen..."

After a while, Wowka, tired of his own stories, announced, "We must turn to smarter literature, shall we say a cousin of the French musketeers, a great writer called Balzac?"

After fifteen minutes of Balzac, Wowka's fans vanished.

The "hot" evening meal was greatly anticipated. It never arrived actually hot, but had at some point in the past connected with a flame. There was the inevitable concentration camp liquid referred to as soup, looking beige, with unspecified floating vegetables and kasha. Also, a slice of bread and a hard-boiled egg. The Russians love tea, which they call chai, a terrific herb they boil in samovars. But our tea here did not deserve its name.

Despite the mostly ghastly food, the meal was enjoyable and buoyant due to two rituals: rolling crumbs and telling jokes. The black, limestone-textured bread was delicious. Any gulag prisoner will attest to it. For starters, it was the only food served to us that contained salt. The bread was distributed in small chunks, as if ripped from a giant loaf. Some of the time it was stale, which did not in any way diminish our enthusiasm for it. We rolled the chunks between our palms until they disintegrated into a pile of crumbs. Luckily, the NKVD had provided each barrack with a table, which was just a wooden board on stilts. But it was better than eating from our beds. Woe to anyone who tried to steal even a crumb from his neighbor.

Let me describe the pleasures of crumbing. First, you generously wet two fingers with saliva and pick up the crumbs the two fingers had collected, stare at them, put them slowly in your mouth. No, no, you do not swallow them, but suck, to prolong the pleasure. Ah, so marvelous!

We added a young priest to our barrack, Father Jerzy Kwiat, a friend of Reb Yossi, son of Reb Eli. Father Jerzy had had a lot of contact with Jews in Bialystok and was attuned to our perception of life. Sucking on his crumbs, he said, "I think this bread was baked when the previous group of prisoners was here."

"Now that's funny," gushed the Count.

Time for jokes. A teacher from Bialystok, Mrs. Horowitz, took a turn. "A teacher in Russia stands in front of his class and asks who wrote Eugene Onegin? "'Comrade Stalin?'" asks one student. "'Wrong!'" thunders the teacher. 'Your turn, Stepan. Who wrote Eugene Onegin?'"

People did not interrupt Mrs. Horowitz's boring joke, because they were engrossed in sucking on their crumbs. I watched my parents putting crumbs into their mouths and noticed again how scabbed and blistery their hands were from work in the quarry.

Mrs. Horowitz continued, but I didn't listen because I already knew who wrote Eugene Onegin. Soon I heard polite laughter, a sign that Mrs. Horowitz had finished.

Count Stankiewicz raised an eyebrow. "You Jews have the most appalling table manners."

"Now that's funny," said the priest.

As good as the crumbs were, they did not provide us kids with enough energy to run around in the heat. I spent much of my time lying on my bed, staring at the wall. A boring wooden wall, with no pictures. The most exciting event was the appearance of a beetle or a cockroach crawling from the wall onto my bed. Cockroaches were best, because here in Siberia they were long and fat—where did they get their food?—scurrying around purposefully, because unlike us kids, they had order in their lives. The kids' game, if you could call it that, was to lie in a circle on our stomachs, cooing endearments to a giant cockroach.

My brother, meanwhile, was despondent, which led him to recklessness. He needed books. Writing anything here was out of the question, because there was no paper, no pencil, no pen, no ink. Wowka kept himself somewhat busy exploring the parameter of Old Mud, and each time he returned with the same report: "Yellow weeds."

Yet each day he disappeared for longer periods of time. If there was nothing, what was he doing out there? One morning I spied on him and saw him enter the NKVD office. Why would a prisoner go to his jailer's office?

Later that week, my question was answered by a surprise visit from Commissar Andrei Ilyich Pamuzov.

"Which bed is Vlodimir Rubinov's?" he barked.

The bed was pointed out. A red-faced Pamuzov grabbed my brother's bed and turned it over. The guard accompanying Pamuzov shook out the blanket and mattress, but found nothing.

Pamuzov took out a penknife and cut up the pillow. Out tumbled a clump of straw, hidden in it a stack of pages.

"Well, you motherfucker." Pamuzov's smile was tinged with acid. The guard assembled the ripped-out pages and placed them on my father's bed. They were mostly pictures and drawings. Wowka lowered his eyes, staring at the floor and shaking like a leaf in a storm.

A terrible comprehension appeared in Father's eyes. Pamuzov turned to him. "Your son, Yakov Markovich, vandalized the N-letter of the Soviet Encyclopedia."

"Why N?"

"Because, Comrade Rubinow, your son apparently thinks that he is Napoleon Bonaparte. Look at these pictures. Napoleon on Elba; Napoleon with his wife Marie Louise…"

"No," Wowka corrected, "this one is Josephine."

Father slapped Wowka across the face. "Why did you do it?"

"I don't know. It just happened."

Father was about to slap Wowka again, but Pamuzov stopped him. "In here, only the NKVD is allowed to hit prisoners." He slapped Wowka on both cheeks.

Mother was clutching my hand so hard I cried out.

"Why did you do it?" Pamuzov hissed at Wowka.

"I don't know."

"You know what I can do to you? I can lock you up in a gulag for the rest of your life on charges of hooliganism."

"But he is only thirteen!" Mother cried stepping forward.

"Comrade Rubinova, this boy is fifteen. I checked your family's papers. Your forgery was not so good."

I was terrified that I would never see Wowka again. Despite everything, I loved my brother. Life would be dull without him. I fell down on my bed and began to cry. Then I saw my mother go down on her knees before Pamuzov, weeping uncontrollably.

"Please, Comrade Commissar, we have been trying to discipline this boy. But this is all my fault. I told him about Napoleon's attack on Russia and he became enamored with War and Peace and everything connected with it. I swear to you that he will never do it again."

It was so quiet in the barrack that I could hear my brother panting.

"No more leisure time for you, young hooligan," said the Commissar at last. "Tomorrow morning you will join the others in the quarry."

The skies opened up in October. The road to the quarry was piled with snow, which was flattened by the prisoners marching in and out of work. The rest of the snow surrounding Old Mud was undisturbed and serenely white, quietly settling into tall, pretty hills. The frost penetrated the barrack through the shattered windows. We were freezing, tiny specks of humanity in a snow-covered tundra.

Food was running low, and the NKVD trucks arrived less frequently. That October, I learned the difference between being hungry and starving. When you're hungry you suffer; but when you starve, you die. Maybe we were already dying, and would soon be buried in this forlorn wilderness.

One evening, as the guards were distributing our bread and lukewarm tea, in strode Commissar Pamuzov, accompanied by his two adjutants. Every advent of Pamuzov signaled trouble. He unfurled a scroll before our eyes. "I am happy to inform you that by special order of Generalissimo Joseph Stalin, you are free men and women! Congratulations!" After a pause, he continued, "Forty kilometers north of here is the city of Biysk. In the morning, we shall bring trucks to take you there."

CHAPTER FOURTEEN

Four trucks arrived at dawn. We hugged and kissed the NKVD for not killing us, then quickly boarded the truck. We rode along an endless snow-covered steppe, the air around us a thick, white mist. Looking at it, you felt no movement or progress, only a subtle gliding toward a mysterious destination. But when the contours of Old Mud disappeared, we realized that we had actually been moving. Wedged between my parents, I burrowed my head in Mother's lap, averting my face from the wind that was slashing the truck's canvas.

Despite it all, I fell asleep. When I woke up darkness had already fallen, and we were at a standstill before a two-story wooden structure.

"Biysk," the NKVD barked.

Father looked at the house in front of us. "Kerosene lamps," he said. "This town has no electricity."

Outside were people swaddled in gray clothing, carrying torches whose glint turned the snow a glowing orange. These townspeople ordered us off the truck and led us into a house that appeared to be a community center, its walls decorated with posters of smiling Red Army boys and girls joyfully marching off to war.

Trained by our stay at Old Mud, my brother and I ran to the nicest corner of the hall and laid claim to it. Our parents followed, with suitcases and bundles in hand.

And there he was, our stalker, our friend, Commissar Pamuzov! Had he adopted us?

"Hello dear free people!" he greeted us. "I have been officially designated NKVD Commissar in charge of former Polish citizens. I shall explain to you how you have so suddenly gone from prisoners to free people."

The crowd in the hall was tired and hungry. Not an excited audience, even if the subject was their own freedom.

"Did you know that you have a Polish government-in-exile located in London?" the Commissar asked. "Of course you didn't. However, this so-called government reached an agreement with the Soviet Union, freeing you from prison. So welcome to Biysk."

Father Jerzy asked, "Comrade Commissar, when can we expect food?"

"I am glad you asked this question, Comrade Priest. You do understand that freedom means you are expected to find work and shelter, so you can feed yourselves. We shall allow you to stay in this auditorium for forty-eight hours and not a minute longer. We shall feed you, of course, but after that you're on your own. A minute later he was gone, followed by the torchbearers. The hall descended into darkness, and after a while we slept.

That night I dreamed of food. Alas, the dream did not materialize. For breakfast the NKVD brought us only buckets of cold water.

Father was the only peppy Pole. He splashed cold water on his face and shook his head like a frisky colt. "I am going into town to find work and an apartment," he announced. "He wrapped a scarf around his neck and left.

With Father gone, the three of us were at a loss. Triumphantly Wowka showed us sheaves of paper with blue ink on them. "I stole them from the Old Mud Office."

Mother was a little curious. "What are they?"

"Blueprints for latrines."

"But they have only outhouses," Mother protested.

"But they have blueprints."

Mother suddenly perked up. "You know children, since we are free, let's go out and explore the city."

Wowka yawned. "I'm not going anywhere in this cold. I must stay here and guard our bundles."

Outside, Mother and I were nearly blinded by the sun, which turned the heaps of snow into iridescent sparkling towers. Next to the Community Center stood two identical wooden buildings: a school and a hospital. On a hill towering over the square, was a sturdy brick structure with a snow-cleared lot, where several trucks and smaller vehicles were parked. Mother's eyes were riveted to a ramshackle hut adjacent to the schoolhouse.

"Pochta," she read excitedly. A post office! A miracle! Unlike Old Mud, Biysk was part of the big world, where people sent and received letters.

"Let's go in and send letters to your aunts Zila and Mina in Palestine," she said.

Inside, the post-office resembled a refurbished barn. A long, narrow room with a low ceiling and walls built of unpolished logs. The floor was covered with a layer of sawdust to absorb the snow that people trampled in from outside. Business was conducted before two low tables. One read "Bank," the other "Letters and Coupons."

Two withered male clerks sat behind each table, a kerosene stove burning dangerously behind their backs. A few wooden stools were scattered around the room, on which several old women sat reading mail or filling out forms. Resolutely Mother approached the "Letters" clerk and said in her best Russian, "Esteemed Comrade Bureaucrat, I would like to mail a letter to Palestine."

"Palestine? Which republic is it in?"

The other clerk raised his bald dome and informed gravely, "Armenia. I happen to know that this Palestine is located in the Soviet Socialist Republic of Armenia."

The mail clerk became angry. "You think you know everything, ha? So let me inform you that Armenian names end with 'an' not, 'ine....'"

Mother set them straight. "Palestine is abroad, across the border."

"Across the border, Comrade Lady? There is no one across the Soviet border except Fascists."

"Oh, no," Mother emphasized, "Palestine is part of England. You know, Anglia. The English fight the Fascists together with the Soviet Union."

"Nonsense, no one fights the Fascists except the Red Army."

People behind us were stirring angrily. I grabbed Mother's hand and tried to pull her out of the line. She refused to budge. Help came from a lady who stood behind us, muffled in layers of home-sewn clothes, including several skirts and a short down jacket neatly patched in a dozen places.

The stranger winked at me. Clearly, she understood my predicament. Turquoise specks in her grey eyes flickered under her heavy wool scarf, spreading a joyful circle of delicate wrinkles.

She stared curiously at my elegant coat with the beaver collar. "Petrovna," the clerk said to my new friend, "I have something for you."

Mother stepped aside, and the lady called Petrovna stood in front of the clerk, who handed her a letter.

"Sign here," he said, placing a nicotine-stained finger on a page in a ledger. The woman bent down and carefully drew a cross. Mother's eyes registered surprise, for she had never before met an illiterate person.

Petrovna put the letter in her jacket's inside pocket and, suddenly weary, dragged her feet into a corner. We followed. She patted my head with a calloused hand.

"How old are you, my dark little Gypsy?" she asked.

"In two months I shall be six. And I am not a Gypsy. I am Polish, and we live in Bialystok. But last night we came here from Old Mud."

Petrovna's hand flew to her mouth. "Good Lord, you poor souls."

Silence lingered, until Petrovna retrieved her letter and

turned it over in her hands. Why was she so afraid to read it? I wondered.

Then she asked Mother, "Can you read Russian, my child?" Slowly she handed over the letter.

My mother began to read aloud. "To Citizen Ludmila Petrovna Vorontseva, greetings…." Abruptly Mother stopped.

"Go on, child. Who is it from?"

"It's from the Commissar of Military Affairs," Mother stammered, her eyes filling with tears. "It says that your son Dimitri Stepanovich Vorontsev is missing in action."

Petrovna leaned heavily against the wall. Mother tried to reassure her. "It only says 'missing in action.' On our train ride we witnessed the confusion of war. No one knows where anyone is."

Petrovna shook her head. "So many dead Russian boys." She breathed hard, forcing herself to calm down. "What are your names?"

"Esfir Yakovlevna Rubinova, and this is my daughter Ralya."

Petrovna replaced her letter in her inside pocket and put on her mittens. Then she turned to me and asked, "Are you hungry, little one?"

I nodded vigorously. Embarassed, Mother fixed her eyes on the floor.

"Follow me to my house, and we shall get you both something to eat."

Outside, Mother pointed to the brick house on the hill. Petrovna crossed herself and whispered, "NKVD."

In Petrovna's company we had our first look at Biysk. It was part of the steppe, and like the rest of it, covered with a thick blanket of snow, mostly undisturbed. Here and there we passed wooden huts. No streets, only meandering crossings shaped by human and animal feet. No evidence that anyone had planned to build here a city. It just happened. Nomads must have stopped here, then settled down. A perfect place for wolves and winds to howl at each other in the night.

After many twists and turns, Petrovna stepped onto a narrow path, which led to a large hut, as nice as any we had passed on our way. Next to the hut stood a straw-covered shed and a chicken coop. Due to the cold, the chickens were heard, not seen. Behind the animal buildings was the now familiar sight of an outhouse. The entire property was surrounded by a low fence, built of sturdy logs.

"My son Borya built this house with his own hands," Petrovna said. "He was killed in action in the beginning of the war." This said, she mounted the steps, and we followed. The door opened onto a large, bright room, in a corner of which was a table and two benches.

A young woman and two little girls sat at the table, bent over what appeared to be schoolwork. They had expected Petrovna home by herself and were startled to see Mother and me.

"This is Yakovlevna," our friend introduced us, "and this is her daughter Ralya. And this is my daughter-in-law Marya, who is married to my son Borya, and their two little girls. Svetya is eight, and Masha is six."

I curtseyed in front of Marya. The girls giggled, and their mother was amused. She and the girls were thin, and I was worried that there might be little food in the house.

"They came here from Old Mud," Petrovna said.

"Oh, dear God!" the young woman cried. "Please, Yakovlevna, sit down. You too, Ralichka."

A wooden icon hung in the corner over the bed, depicting an orange-haired Jesus with a long face and pointy chin.

"Don't be afraid, Yakovlevna; you can pray to him," Petrovna smiled. "The NKVD don't know that we have an icon."

Mother looked at her with concern. "We are Jews."

Petrovna and Marya looked stunned. "Jesus Christ Almighty!" cried Petrovna. "We have never met a Jew before. This is wonderful! You are the ancient people of the Bible. We are very honored."

Mother and I exchanged glances. Petrovna reached under the bed and withdrew a padlocked trunk. Out of it came an old book with a black cover and a gold cross in the middle.

"You see; we have a Bible." She patted it tenderly and put it back in the trunk.

The girls wanted to play, but Petrovna said that Mother and I must eat first. Oh, I thought, I love you, Petrovna! She busied herself at the stove, stirring something in a frying pan. The forgotten smell of cooked food hit my nostrils with such impact that I thought I might faint. Mother closed her eyes, breathing hard.

Petrovna brought over two plates, on each a fried egg and a large slice of bread thickly spread with butter. Svetya and Masha fetched mugs of warm milk. Transfixed, I stared at the yolk, until I felt a hand touching my hair.

"It's all right, child. You can eat your food."

The spell was broken. I punctured the yolk and watched as

the yellow spread into the white. I stuffed my mouth with bread and butter, washing it down with a long gulp of milk. The fried egg was the best food I had ever eaten. When I stopped long enough to catch my breath, I saw that Mother had eaten her egg and drunk the milk, but left her bread untouched.

"Do you have other family, Yakovlevna?" our new friend asked. Mother nodded. "Eat, you need your strength. We'll give you bread to take with you."

Marya went over to the cupboard and returned with a chunk of bread wrapped in cloth. Her other hand held a bottle of milk. She gave it to Mother.

"For your family."

So this was it? It was time to go? Unable to restrain myself, I put my head on the table and began to cry.

"Where do you live?" Petrovna asked Mother. She shouldn't have, because Mother also burst into tears. If it were not for our tears, we would have walked out of Petrovna's house gratefully clutching our gifts.

But then, of course, the rest of our lives would have been different.

CHAPTER FIFTEEN

I often wondered if, after meeting Father and Wowka, Petrovna regretted asking us to come live with her. Masha, the little one, gulped and asked Wowka, "Uncle, where do you end?" Russian kids call adult men and women "aunt" and "uncle."

We discovered that there was another member of the Vorontsev family, Anushka, the wife of Petrovna's younger son Dimitri, whose "missing in action" letter had brought us together. Anushka was beautiful, like the Paris doll that Father had brought me, and Wowka had left behind when we were deported.

My first thought on seeing Anushka was: Please, God, when I grow up make me as beautiful as Anushka! She was blond, with the kind of tendrils you see on cameos, one of which I had seen Mother wear. Also, her skin was like Snow White's, and mine was something Mother called olive. So, I don't believe that even God could have made me look like Anushka.

When introducing Anushka, Petrovna said, "Anushka is the best cow girl in Biysk. She has two prized cows, Rusalka and

Ludmila. She and Dima were married a short time before he went to fight the war."

Anushka's face brightened at the mention of her husband's name. Clearly, the letter was still a secret. Anushka lived in one of the hut's two bedrooms, hers with its own outside door and porch. The other bedroom was Petrovna's. Marya and her daughters, my new friends Svetya and Masha, lived in the main room, which the Russians call the "bright" room, the one with the table and oven.

For us, Petrovna gave up her hard-earned privacy. "I will be happier with Marya and the girls. Sleeping alone in a room is too frightening."

We settled into Petrovna's bedroom, which was about the size of my nursery in Bialystok. There was one metal bed, same as we had in Old Mud, but cleaner. Mother and I could sleep there together.

"We'll get another bed for Wowka and Yakov Markovich," she said.

Oh, my God, Father and Wowka in one bed!

Petrovna spread word around town that two big, strong men lived with them now, so robbers beware. Her admiration for Father deepened with his announcement that he must immediately find work to pay for food and rent. The one industry in Biysk was the Lenin Sugar Beet Factory, which explained why our Old Mud tea had been sweetened.

After an initial visit to the plant, Father returned with the good news that he had been granted an appointment with the manager for the next day. Hearing this, Marya wrote a note and handed it to Father. "Borya, my late husband, and Oleg Vladimirovich, the director, were very good friends," she said. "Borya was the most productive foreman and also head of the Communist Union in the plant. Tell Oleg that I am sending my warmest greetings."

More instructions from Marya: "When you look for a job in our country, you must remember to lie about everything. You do not tell them that you were a successful businessman in Poland, or that you hold a university degree, even if it is from a Communist university. Tell them that you have always been a working man who happens to be good with numbers."

It worked. Father was hired as a bookkeeper. He offered Petrovna a nice share of his salary for rent and living expenses. This increased the family's income, which till that point had consisted of Marya's job as a feltcher, a physician's assistant, in the hospital located near the post office.

"You may call me Dr. Vorontseva," Marya said with a grin. "The army drafted the doctors, and the hospitals everywhere rely on us feltchers."

"My sister Fanya would have loved such a job," Mother reflected, and her eyes moistened. Indeed, Marya must have been important, because the hospital truck brought over two beds, mattresses, blankets and sheets.

A week after we moved in, Anushka erupted into tears, and the rest of the family followed. The secret was out. Petrovna had revealed that Dima was missing, which in this war was as good as dead. Mother wept, Father looked forlorn, and Wowka left the house to take a walk through the snow.

No one slept that night because of Anushka's grief. Having kept the letter in the inside pocket of her jacket for a few weeks, Petrovna had calmed down a little. But giving Anushka the news without warning plunged the young woman into despondency. Her attempts to be brave made the ordeal worse. She cried all by herself, throughout the night, walking the wooden planks of her bedroom.

Such grief made me curious about her husband, Dima. In a strange way, Mother and I felt a closeness to him since we were present when the letter arrived. Seeing Anushka outside tending to the cows, I slipped into her bedroom and soon found what I was looking for. On the commode was Anushka's and Dima's wedding picture. Oh, they were so beautiful! She was blond and delicate; Dima was dark-haired, with a huge grin and eyes that seemed to dance around as if afraid to miss something.

Petrovna came up behind me, and I blushed. "I'm sorry I came in here without asking permission. I wanted to see his picture."

"Ralichka, you are like all the girls. Big or small, all were attracted to my Dima."

"Was he nice?"

"He was very nice, but he always wanted more than he had. He wanted things, to own, to buy, and Russia is not a country for things. We are a poor country invaded by Fascists. No one knows why."

"And how was Borya?"

"Oh, Borya was an angel."

Crying over Dima ebbed with time, but still continued under the surface. I thought they might be wrong. "If he is missing, he will return," I told Svetya and Masha, in what I considered a voice of hope. It worked. The two must have been comforted, because they stopped crying.

Children of Polish deportees, even though officially free, were forbidden to attend school for fear we might contaminate the minds of innocent young Communists. My brother, now sixteen, disappeared each day. My parents did not ask where he went, because they had nothing to offer him. Still they guessed, correctly, that their son had become acquainted with hooligans his age, since boys under eighteen were the only healthy men left in town.

Opportunities for mischief abounded. The town had received not only Polish deportees, but also Ukrainians, many with clothing and jewelry the likes of which the town had never seen. The temptation for robbery was daunting. The dissolute youths roamed the paths, and my brother roamed with them.

Luckily, we had not been robbed. But a danger greater than the gangs was redeeming coupons for our daily bread rations. Our ability to do so would determine how long—and how well—we could survive. Once a day Mother and Petrovna walked from the hut to the bread depot. Success or failure depended on the length of the breadline and the availability of supplies.

Several rules applied to this daily routine. One, if you lost a day, for whatever reason, you could not redeem it the next day. Two, only adults were allowed to receive the bread, and only for members of their immediate families. During the first two months of our stay in Biysk, the authorities had enough bread for a day's distribution. But when the cold intensified, supply lines were interrupted, and our rations were harder to obtain.

"The poor Russian people are starving again," Petrovna sighed, "just like in the revolutionary wars."

The bread depot opened at six each morning, but the line

formed as early as four. Many women left their children in line and relieved them when the windows opened. On many occasions Svetya, Masha and I were left in line to keep the place for Petrovna and Mother. From one dark morning to the next, the breadline was becoming an ever-scarier place. Sometimes a small child would be found in the snow, frozen to death. People were heard saying vicious things, such as, if you leave your babies here, you can blame no one but yourself for their death. Once we saw a frozen child tossed aside to clear the way for those pushing ahead. At other times, they would toss a living child, to no one's surprise or indignation.

A danger greater than the frost was the presence of teenage gangs, which daily terrorized the breadline. Too lazy to stand in line, they robbed at knifepoint people who had already received their rations, ending up with more bread than they and their families could eat. A brisk bread trade had been formed on the black market. Resisting the gangs would often end in injury or death. It was smarter to obey.

For Svetya, Masha and me, duty at the breadline ended with our discovery of the old man's corpse. We came upon him one morning at dawn, having been relieved by Mother and Petrovna. Heading back home, we walked at a brisk pace, our faces muffled with heavy scarves. Suddenly the sun burst through the clouds, casting the snowfield in metallic blue. Then Masha stopped abruptly.

"What?" asked Svetya angrily, because we were not supposed to stop in this cold for fear of freezing our toes. Masha pointed to what was clearly a corpse. He was a man, naked, grey and shriveled. "I think he's frozen through and through," Svetya said expertly.

"Do you think he was murdered," I questioned, "or just robbed of his clothes and left to die?"

My question remained unanswered, because Masha was vomiting into the snow.

"Stop it!" Svetya cried, as she ran over to move the scarf from her sister's face. Masha sat down in the snow next to the corpse. Though Masha was my age, Svetya and I felt honor-bound to protect her. We pulled her up and wiped her mouth with snow, then readjusted the scarf. We put her between us and dragged her along.

"You know," said Svetya, "this is not only my first corpse, but my first naked man."

"Disgusting," I said, and Masha started crying.

When Petrovna and Mother returned with the bread, Svetya and I told them animatedly about our discovery of the corpse. They were shocked, though by now Svetya and I sounded as if we had become accustomed this sight.

"You sound like flesh-eaters," Petrovna said.

And that's how our duty at the breadline came to an end. Mother and Petrovna went early by themselves, each carrying a sharp knife.

Then a miracle occurred. Wowka had befriended a revolting gang called the Black Cats, so named because they wore gloves with spikes sticking out of them. With these gloves they scratched the faces of those they wanted to rob or intimidate. Wowka became their messenger of love, writing letters for gang members, the contents of which made the girls swoon.

As payment, the Cats shielded Wowka from harm and made

sure that Petrovna and Mother received their daily bread without interference.

CHAPTER SIXTEEN

loved our Russian stove, the one responsible for cooking my first egg. This device came in three parts: the stovetop where the egg was fried, then the oven where we roast meat, which is largely unavailable, and where we tried to bake a cake with flour, which was normally unavailable. The stove's third function was as a shelter on top, an alcove with blankets, where children slept to escape the cold. The wind may have howled outside and frost may have coated the windows, but it was snug and warm in our blessed cocoon.

I spent more time up there than Svetya and Masha, because they went to school six days a week, but I remained home. My biggest fear was that I was destined to remain stupid for the rest of my life. I was six years and two months old, yet still unable to read or write. Mother said that Wowka could do all this at age four, or maybe he entered the world reciting Pushkin.

My dream was to learn how to read, so I could go to the library and borrow a book. But who would teach me? Mother was jumpy and nervous, Father spent most of his days in the factory; Wowka was never around.

"He's out with his hooligan friends," Father would say. "If he gets one of their girlfriends pregnant, he's dead."

Marya worked in the hospital and brought work home; Petrovna was illiterate; Anushka might have also been, and Svetya and Masha didn't know enough to teach anyone.

The deportees' unofficial leaders were Reb Eli, young Father Jerzy Kwiat, and the oh-so-noble Count Stankiewicz. The three petitioned Commissar Pamuzov to admit us Polish kids into their regular school. Absolutely nyet, said Pamuzov. But he suggested that we set up an afternoon shift for deportee children, which could be taught by deportee adults.

It was a bad idea, but there was no other. Our shift started at two p.m., when the town was already in partial darkness, and ended at four, but it might have just as well been midnight. When our little school started, I informed Mr. Zygmund Kobielski, a saddle maker in Bialystok and now a Polish literature teacher, that someone must teach me immediately how to read Russian, so I could go to the library and borrow a book.

Mr. Kobielski gave me a sorrowful look. "I am so sorry, Rala, but I don't know any Russian."

"It can't be. Everyone in Bialystok speaks Russian."

He laughed. "Your people speak Russian. We Poles are too proud to have ever learned. Perhaps Jews are right to consider us stupid. Anyway, I suggest that you speak to Mr. Ginsburg. He teaches math, but he surely knows Russian."

Mr. Ginsburg agreed. "I shall be honored to teach the granddaughter of Rabbi Jacob Meyer Rakowski, even if I have to do it on the side and in the dark." I didn't bother to ask what "on the side" meant, because I didn't care on what side I would learn to read Russian.

We decided that he and I would arrive at school fifteen minutes early and read from the primers he must have stolen somewhere. He would also lengthen the break, so we could study some more.

"You are a very smart child," he said. "Your grandfather would be proud of you." I was immediately swept up by memories.

There was also the matter of how to get to the school and back. Mother freed up some time and took me there. The way back came from an unexpected quarter: my brother. He, of course, would have nothing to do with this school, and the instructors would have nothing to do with him. But since the end of school was near suppertime, Wowka volunteered to bring me home.

It worked for a while. But one Wednesday afternoon, my brother failed to show up. By then everyone had left. After waiting a bit longer, abandoned alone in this dark and frightening building, I had no choice but to venture home on my own. Outside it was pitch black, the only light coming from silver rays shimmering on piles of snow. I wrapped my scarf around my face and pushed on.

Sometime into my journey, the wind began to howl, lifting the snow and circling it in the air. My heart pounded as I realized that this was the buran, the most frightening storm a Siberian winter produced. I had seen it before, but always from inside the hut. Standing in the middle of it was like being attacked by a white avalanche.

And then I died.

At least that's what I thought. The only reason I didn't die was the appearance of a Kirgiz tribesman who heard my screams and dug me out of the snow. The Kirgiz were a tribe that lived on top of Mount Altai, the one that kept guard on us in Old Mud. These tribespeople were small and slanty-eyed, and the men wore floppy hats.

I might have been unconscious when my savior first put me in his sled. When I came to and saw him, I panicked, remembering the tales Svetya had told me about Kirgiz men who murder their wives, cut them up, and stuff them into suitcases. At this moment it came to me that not all Kirgiz owned suitcases. In the meantime, I enjoyed the smooth gliding of the sled, a pleasure interrupted by persistent whistling snow.

"You are home," said the Kirgiz in a sweet voice. He lifted me out of the sled and took me to the bright room. They were sitting there in a frightened circle, waiting for Wowka and me. Everyone jumped and hugged me, Mother most of all. Clearly, they had thought that they would never see me again.

Father offered the Kirgiz some money, but he refused and returned to his sled.

My teeth were chattering so badly I couldn't speak. Mother undressed me and bundled me up with blankets. Petrovna brought a mug of lukewarm tea and told me to drink slowly.

"And think good thoughts. That is most important for recovery."

Wowka had not yet arrived, but everyone was thinking about what he had done. Fists clenched, Father said, "This time I'll kill him."

An hour later Wowka showed up, jauntily shaking off his hat and jacket. He stared at me with surprise, as if he had totally forgotten of my existence. Looking at us intently, he said with unease, "Look Mama, I can explain. I was there, at the school, I swear to God, maybe a little late, but I looked for Rala everywhere…"

Father's fist landed on his neck with fury. The next blow was just as fierce.

Petrovna grabbed Father's arm before he could strike Wowka a third time. "Yakov Markovich, you cannot kill your son."

Father looked at her and nodded.

Almost dying in the snow brought my schooling to an abrupt end. Still, the time I had spent there was worthwhile, because somehow Mr. Ginsburg had taught me enough reading skills so that I was making plans to visit the library as soon as the snows ended.

Since I was not allowed to go to school, I pumped Svetya and Masha about their classes. I transferred all their knowledge into my head, plus something extra: lice. With this achievement, I was invited to join their lice-killing ritual. First, Svetya fetched a knife with a dull blade.

"I shall demonstrate on Masha how good we Russians are at killing lice," she said.

Masha got down on her knees and lowered her head.

"All ready for the guillotine!" Wowka shouted. Father looked at him as if he himself were a louse.

Svetya spread her sister's hair, pulling hard on both ends. "Look hard, Ralya, and you will see tiny white creatures feasting on Masha's scalp." Sure enough, plump little dots were busily scurrying around. "Now, I shall begin the killing!"

Svetya lowered the knife at an angle and bore down on Masha's exposed skin. An ominous crunch resounded in the room. People applauded.

"Let's count how many we kill." We counted so many dead lice that we almost lost count. Now was my turn to kill, as Svetya moved away and offered me Masha's scalp.

"As long as you remember that I have never done this before," I warned.

Masha was scared. "Let me out! Ralya is too clumsy."

"No, I am not." I grabbed Masha's hair and started crunching with enthusiasm.

Soon Svetya killed my lice, and I killed hers.

"Well girls," said Petrovna, "bring home more lice, and we'll have another evening of fun."

CHAPTER SEVENTEEN

The combined families of Vorontsevs and Rubinovs needed more income. Mother felt guilty for not contributing to the household, so she decided to become a capitalist. What it meant was to sell the clothes we had brought with us from Bialystok.

"First the cloth samples," Father said, "these I shall sell myself."

He left the house on Sunday carrying the samples, and returned home empty-handed, his pockets stuffed with rubles.

Next, the lingerie. Selling it was painful for Mother. Lovingly she smoothed each nightgown and lace pantie, then sighed, "So it goes."

Marya discreetly spread the word that such-and-such luxurious merchandise made in Paris was available for sale. Within twenty-four hours, the Vorontsev home was overrun by the wives and mistresses of local NKVD officers, Communist party functionaries, and generals posted at the local Red Army garrison.

Wowka showed great interest in the sale. Hidden behind a

window, he observed the women's purchases and was excited when they tried on the merchandise. He described this to me in detail. "Pamuzov's 'kept' bought a black peignoir and silk stockings, but no panties," he reported.

"So what?"

Wowka just laughed.

On Sunday, as Wowka and his hooligans snuck into a ball of local dignitaries, they noticed the barrack commander's beefy wife valiantly struggling to breathe in my mother's pink negligee. And when she danced, the lace on her bosom broke loose, turning the event into a local legend.

Together with Father's samples, the sale yielded enough money to ease our lives for a few months. Yet Petrovna insisted that Mother keep a large portion of the money. "Yakovlevna, keep the rest for a rainy day." I thought she should have said "a snowy day," but it didn't make sense either way.

"Do you know what lesson I learned from the lingerie sale?" Mother looked at Petrovna and Marya.

"A lesson. Very interesting," said Petrovna.

"That Siberian women have really huge breasts."

"I haven't noticed." Marya looked at her flat chest.

Mother persisted, "My point is that no one here makes brasseries."

"Yakovlevna, no one here makes anything."

The size of Siberian breasts awakened Mother's ambitions, as befit a graduate of the Warsaw Brasserie Academy. As a true capitalist, she surely dreamed of making a million rubles.

No one knew Marya's sources of obtaining "things," so no one was surprised when she handed Mother several large sheets of drawing paper. Armed with it, Mother purposefully marched into the library and found a manual on brasserie-making, containing a five-page essay by Comrade Stalin about the importance of textiles in winning the war against the Fascists.

Further in the book Mother found the basic patterns for constructing medium, large and extra-large brasseries. She copied everything into Marya's papers. At home, she made additional patterns from pages of Pravda.

"Dear old Pravda," Father remarked. "The other great use for it is the outhouse. Pravda after all means truth."

At the next stage, Mother bought a sewing machine from a seamstress who had gone blind. She took some money from the bundle under the mattress and bought a roll of sturdy white cotton on the black market. The first couple of brasseries were constructed for imaginary breasts. Then it was time to have live models. The only one to qualify was Anushka, whom Mother declared a "medium." Blushing, Anushka ran off.

Still, there was progress. Mother was thrilled, because now her brasseries looked like brasseries, and she was emboldened to task Marya with passing the word to her sources from the lingerie sale that Comrade Yakovlevna had opened a salon for custom-made brasseries. The customers returned in droves, and Mother braced for an avalanche of rubles.

Soon, however, she discovered that it was a lot easier to sew brasseries for imaginary breasts than for real ones. She measured the breasts, measured the cotton, and muttered a prayer, most likely to Grandfather. She huffed, the clients huffed—after which Mother gave them a date to return for a fitting. The fittings were successful, and money exchanged hands.

Not unexpectantly, the parade of breasts threatened to turn my brother into a lunatic. He neglected his hooligans and spent time outside the window, watching the women coming and going. I was sure he had naughty thoughts.

"Look, Ralka," he wheedled. "If you tell me when something good is coming, I'll give you a present."

"What kind of present?"

"Next time my friends and I sneak into a movie, I'll take you along."

I agreed, because I had never seen a movie. Problem: What is good? For me, all the breasts were boring. Yet I had to make a selection. On second thought, the breasts of the "kepts" were nicer than those of the wives. I was right, and Wowka was delighted. He managed to squeeze himself in between the two windows in the bright room—and STARE!

I demanded that he pay up and take me to see a movie. So, one afternoon, he asked permission from Mother to take me to his friend Alyosha's house to meet his sister, who was my age. "They are from Kiev and very cultured."

Mother agreed. "But you must bring her home early."

Outside he confided that we were going to the movies and not to meet Alyosha's sister, because Alyosha didn't have a sister. "He is a muzhik, like everyone here." Muzhik is an insulting word for peasant.

At the Community Center, (where we had spent our first night in Biysk), was also used as a movie house. we met Alyosha and his two friends, their faces covered with disgusting pimples.

"They're my bodyguards," Wowka whispered.

We snuck into the hall and settled in the back. It was an American movie, "Sun Valley Serenade," in which a woman called Sonia danced ballet on ice. I was puzzled. In Siberia we had tons of ice, but no one danced on it. Maybe the Americans were cleverer than the Russians. But I could not say it out loud, because someone might denounce me and send us back to Old Mud. My brother whispered that in the movie, a man called Glenn Miller played the best trombone in the world. Listening to the music, my brother cried.

During the intermission we mingled with the crowd, pretending to belong. Suddenly a bone-chilling gust of wind ushered in a wild-looking girl, her red hair covered with icicles. Her eyes roamed, then zeroed in on someone. She stopped and produced a sharp kitchen knife from inside her jacket. With it in her outstretched arm, she rushed toward a girl in a yellow sweater, whom I had earlier seen embracing a soldier. The girl with the red hair plunged the knife into the chest of the girl in the yellow sweater.

"Bitch, bitch, bitch!" screamed the attacker, as she continued to strike the fallen victim, whose blood soon covered her yellow sweater.

I screamed.

Alyosha moved fast. "We must go before the attendant discovers that we snuck in."

My brother balked. "No, I must stay. This may be my last chance to hear Glenn Miller."

"No Wowka, we're going," Alyosha persisted.

My brother was stunned. This was obviously the first time

that this hooligan had dared to contradict him. But he was also scared. Alyosha picked me up in his arms, and we ran out of the building.

Wowka and I pretended that we had a wonderful time with Alyosha's little sister. My parents had sat on their bed, waiting. "You were supposed to be here earlier," Father chastised him.

"Father, we saw a movie," I said excitedly. "An American movie with a ballerina on ice. But we didn't see the whole movie, because the girl with the red hair killed the girl in the yellow sweater."

"In the movie?" Mother asked.

"No, in the corridor during intermission."

Silence.

"Look, it wasn't my fault," Wowka was agitated. "Ralka caught me looking at the naked women and blackmailed me to take her to the movies."

"You degenerate!" Father was at the height of his anger. "Breasts! Is that all you can think about? Your people are in exile, and you dream about breasts! God will get you for it!"

I had never before heard Father utter the word "God."

"This is all my fault," Mother said, "It is I who introduced breasts and ruined this family's well-being. The brasserie salon is closing."

"Ralya watched a girl get murdered!" Svetya and Masha spread the story in school. With each retelling, the account became more and more gruesome, and the river of blood soon gushed like an ocean.

One morning, Svetya and Masha urged me to come to school

with them. "By special invitation of the teacher," they lied. And there I was, a guest in the school I was not allowed to attend. Very elaborately I went through every second of that evening, describing vividly every drop of blood, the girl falling down in slow motion…

I had never imagined that witnessing a murder would make me popular.

CHAPTER EIGHTEEN

The deportees organized into a group they called the Committee of Bialystock Deportees, whose representatives would perhaps carry more weight in persuading Commissar Pamuzov to allow our children attend Russian schools.

The good news spread like a wind through the deportee community. Yes, in the autumn I would be in school with Svetia and Masha! Also, my smarter-than-everyone brother would be forced to attend.

In the meantime, as summer lingered on, we spent a great deal of time outdoors. It was sunflower season, the stalks tall and perfect. If God had indeed created them, he had done a splendid job. I examined them carefully, the seedy black centers surrounded by tiny yellow leaves. My grandmother Jadwiga would have made a dress in these colors. Not a petal out of order, every stalk proud and unbent. I could hide in them, and no one would find me. I pretended to be a sunflower—get out of my species and become a huge, pretty flower, even if just for a day.

Elated by such pleasant thoughts, I failed to notice that I had wandered far away from home and onto the open road. The sound of footsteps behind me restored me to reality. I heard several pairs of feet, loud and decisive. This might have meant danger, but I wasn't sure. I slowed down, and the footsteps changed to a lazy shuffle. I became terrified and ran. The feet behind me ran faster. Suddenly a hand grabbed the bottom of my dress and threw me onto the road. I felt a stinging pain as my knees hit the pebbles. Looking up, I saw Wowka's friend Alyosha, who had gone with us to the movies. With him were two teenage boys I had never seen.

I pulled myself up to my feet. "Alyosha, it's me, Rala, Wowka's sister."

"Your brother is a dirty Jew traitor who is no longer our friend," he said. "He joined our sworn enemies the Red Roosters and is telling them our secrets."

I stared at them. What on earth was he talking about? Then he said something I understood even less. "You Jews killed our Lord Jesus Christ."

"Jesus Christ is on the icon in our bright room!" I shouted.

This made them madder. Understanding little but frightened a lot, I took off down the road, my knees bleeding from the fall. They caught up with me in no time. Alyosha grabbed me from behind and turned me around. He spit in my face, leaving a disgusting glob on my cheek. I couldn't get rid of it because another boy held my arms. The third boy brought Aloysha a fistful of pebbles, with which he scratched that same cheek. It hurt, and I burst out crying. Alyosha shrugged, and the troika departed.

I'm going to die, I told myself as I ran. I'll lose all my blood and die on the road. Yet, somehow I made it home alive.

"No," Petrovna answered me emphatically, "you did not kill Jesus Christ."

I kept it a secret that the beating was connected to Wowka's treacherous deeds. By now I was too tired to watch Father beat him up, yelling vile peasant curses.

"Three ugly hooligans beat me up," was all I said. But how could I prevent another beating? "Mama," I continued, "how can I please stop being Jewish?"

Mother, who rarely laughed since leaving Bialystok, found my request amusing. "Darling, there is no way out of being Jewish. It's a life sentence."

In September, I enthusiastically marched off to school with Svetia and Masha. I was a happy sunflower again, dancing on a cloud.

"What a nuisance," was Wowka's reaction to the idea of attending school.

A man came to class to hand out red ties and tin badges with burning logs on them. We put them on our shirts. We looked at each other; no question, everyone looked better. The man stood by the blackboard, squinted at the sun, and said, "Good morning, children, I am your Communism teacher. From now on, you are happy young Oktyabronoks, which means Children of the October Revolution. Your loyalty is not—I repeat, not—to your parents, brothers or sisters. Certainly not to your aunts, ha ha ha! Your allegiance is only to Mother Russia and Comrade Stalin. So, listen closely. If you hear your mother or father speak badly about Comrade Stalin, you must come to me and denounce them."

"I'm supposed to denounce you," I told Wowka, as we trudged

back from school.

"In that case, I'll tell the NKVD that you are a follower of Leon Trotsky."

"Who is he?"

"Ask your father."

"Papa, who is Leon Trotsky?" It was late at night, and we were already in bed, though not asleep. Father jumped out of bed and pulled Wowka by his hair. I had seen rage in my father for years, but this time it was part terror.

"So, what if I said Tr...?" Father smashed Wowka across the face before he could pronounce the full name. He ripped off his clothes and hit him in his chest and stomach. This time, Mother did not interfere.

Father spoke through clenched teeth. "Never, ever, pronounce this name. This applies to everyone, to every person who lives in the Soviet Union. You have never heard this word, you cannot dream about it, erase it from your minds!"

He looked at Wowka for the first time since the beating started. "If anyone hears the word, we shall immediately be shot. Even you, Rala, and the entire Vorontsev family."

Mother nodded.

I loved being in school and believed that the red tie was a great addition to my drab calico dress. The honor of being a Child of the October Revolution interested me little. For me, the most exciting sensation of school was being with so many children in this building and in the playground. Marching, playing, singing, gossiping during recess—all terrific. I was diligent at learning secrets, so I could honestly contribute to the gossip. In this respect, Svetya and Masha were very helpful.

Memorizing was a big function of education. Just how important it was we learned in the matter of the national anthem. When I started school, the Soviet anthem was the "Internationale," a hymn about miserable people, such as "the downtrodden, slaves, hungry, poor." After Svetya, Masha and I had learned the morbid list by heart, we felt relieved.

But not for long.

Two weeks after we had committed the Internationale to memory, the Soviet Union changed its anthem to something timely and blood-stirring. And long! It consisted of three long stanzas, with three refrains, each just a little different from the others, to make it harder to remember.

Our teacher, Olga Maksimovna, had this sage advice: "Forget the Internationale immediately. Wipe it out of your memory!"

The new anthem was a war song with simpler words than the Internationale. Its purpose was to make people happy to go fight the Fascists and die for Mother Russia and Comrade Stalin. Svetya, Masha and I learned one stanza each, and we were the first in class to volunteer. Our trio was a success. We swore to Olga Maksimovna that within a week each of us would know the three stanzas. In reality, it took us more than a month.

CHAPTER NINETEEN

Mail! The Rubinows received a letter! The letter was so special that it was delivered to Father at work. At home, the Rubinows and Vorontsevs sat down to read it. It was from my uncle Marek Rakowski, whom we had last seen at the Bialystok Railroad Station. The paper shook in Mother's hands, and she had to sit down. "My dear sister Fira, Kuba, Wowka and Rala. The bloodthirsty Huns did not get the indomitable Marek Rakowski. Once or twice they came close, breathing their foul schnapps down my neck, but our glorious Trans-Siberian Railroad outran the Luftwaffe. Note to censor: This letter contains nothing but love for Mother Russia."

Marya wrinkled her forehead. "Yakovlevna, ask your brother how he could smell schnapps on the Germans' breath, when they were flying above in an airplane?"

"My brother is a writer, and his profession is to exaggerate."

Marek reported that he had stayed with the soldiers for a week. When the brigade was dispatched to the front, he stayed behind and made his way to Kuybishov, a safe city to which many Soviet offices and agencies had been relocated. One of these agencies was the all-powerful "Cominform Bureau," the Communist propaganda/information arm. They recruited Marek immediately.

"How did he find us?" Mother wondered.

"Cominform can find anyone," Wowka replied.

Reb Eli was ninety-two when he died. We were shocked. He had been joking so much about dying that we became convinced he would live forever. The Polish Committee reorganized, naming Count Stankiewicz its President, and Father Kwiat Vice-President. The priest refused, suggesting that Reb Yossi, Reb Eli's son, should be Vice-President. Father Kwiat and Yakov Rubinow continued as members.

In this part of the world winter sets in gradually, and in me it found an avid watcher. My first weather conclusion: Today is colder than yesterday, and tomorrow will be colder than today. The government admitted that Father Winter was a Red Army ally.

Wowka disdained the students and teachers in school, referring to them as "Bolshevik morons." At first it amused him to make jokes at their expense and watch their mortified reactions, but after a while, even this was boring. So Wowka hit on a creative idea. He marched in to see his class teacher Ilya Vlodimirovich Timoshenko.

"Comrade Teacher, I would like to do some independent study, extensive research and a written thesis on the subject of the Red Army's offensive against the White Russians in the years 1917-19. The title page will indicate that this work was suggested and supervised by you."

Vlodimir Rubinov delivered. His thesis was long, and if anyone had actually read it, they would have found a profound analysis of the two years after the October Revolution. Nothing like this had ever been written by a Biysk student. The school principal and Commissar Pamuzov—the Commissar had the habit of making himself a partner to every achievement—sent the essay to the Siberian capital, Novossibirsk, where the Education Commissar pronounced my brother an instant high school graduate with a "golden diploma," that is, solid "fives" top to bottom, the highest grade in Russia. Wowka received a railroad ticket to travel to the capital for an interview about his future.

He returned home with an announcement that his future had been charted by the Altai Regional Communist Party. In his hands was an acceptance certificate from the University of Novossibirsk, to start as soon as they could find him a dormitory and a meal plan. His major: naval engineering.

Father burst out laughing. "That's great! Novossibirsk is landlocked."

Who were we? By "we," I mean the motley crew who had come here from Bialystok between 1939 and 1941. We used to be citizens of the Polish Republic, but it had disappeared in the fall of 1939. When we were carried off to Siberia, we became stateless deportees, without passports or identity cards. Having been supposedly liberated, we were under the thrall of a bunch of Polish generals and politicians, themselves exiled to London. Everyone wanted us—in a relationship without benefits.

These might have been questions the Soviet authorities were

asking themselves. And the result was an order to force on us Soviet citizenship. The decision was important enough to be published in Pravda. Commissar Pamuzov and his deputies appeared before the Polish Committee with an order to have every former Polish citizen register at the NKVD office on the hill, where he would be issued an identity card with a hammer and sickle on it.

An emergency meeting was convened in Father Kwiat's house. I tagged along, but not Wowka. Just as well. Father did not need his acidic views. The meeting started with singing the Polish National Anthem. "Poland will stand forever/ As long as we are here…" Count Stankiewicz recited the Soviet demands, and the attendees booed with patriotic outrage.

"We shall never surrender Polish honor!" someone shouted. Also: "We shall fight this indignity with our last breath!"

I noticed a smirk on Father's face. He stood up and asked, "Dear Count, did Pamuzov specify the punishment in case we refuse?"

Stankiewicz was surprised, as if the thought had never occurred to him. "Well, he did not threaten per se, but he repeated several times that we should accept the offer for our children's sake. And Rubinow, since you are such an authority on all things Russian, you know that they are gaming us, and the best response is immediate rejection. Now, let's vote!"

"Just a minute!" my father responded. "Let me swear to you that if the Soviets decide on a course of action, nothing will sway them. Look at the way they fight the Germans. They may be losing a million soldiers, but in the end they will win the war. So if we cherish our children's lives, let's go home and cool off."

As a result of Father's speech, the Committee decided that

Reb Yossi and Father Kwiat would ask the authorities for a week's delay.

Before the week was up, Father came from the plant with a bizarre tale. "I was summoned to the plant manager's office, where in attendance was also our beloved Commissar Pamuzov. On the table was my file. The NKVD never speak with you without the menacing presence of your file.

"The Commissar opened the file and told me everything about myself, also the history of the Rubinows and Rakowskis. No surprise—the Russians hoard information, even if startlingly useless. On to the matter of the Soviet identity cards. Pamuzov said, 'You must appreciate that the cards will give you all the benefits of Soviet citizenship...'"

Petrovna and Marya joined our laughter.

Father cont6inued, "Pamuzov finished with this: 'I have orders to distribute these cards, and I shall follow these orders no matter what.' This threat could be hardly called veiled."

The next time the Committee met was in Reb Yossi's hut. After a week's meditation, the people were equally split for and against. Father knew it was up to him. "We must accept reality. What the Soviets need in every endeavor is victory. If not, we'll end up in the gulag, compared to which Old Mud is a resort. For ourselves and our children, we must survive till this war ends, and we return home."

No boos this time. An uneasy silence prevailed while the assembled considered their decision. Grudgingly, not looking at Father, they voted "yes" to the identity cards. Father Kwiat did not vote.

The Rubinows' identity cards were imprinted "Jew."

Father's troubles with his Polish countrymen continued. Although to a man they accepted the cards, they blamed Father for their betrayal of Poland by referring to him as "the Jew traitor." Mostly, they blamed him for Father Kwiat's disappearance. We became aware that the priest was gone when he failed to show up at the following Committee meeting. Everyone headed to the priest's hut, and found it boarded up with a sign on the door: "No entry by order of the NKVD."

A few days later, Father was summoned again to the plant manager's office—naturally, with Pamuzov. "We thank you, Yakov Markovich, for the fine service you had rendered to Comrade Stalin and our homeland."

On the table was a cardboard box from which emerged smells of freshly ground coffee, chocolate and vanilla cookies. Father had not smelled anything like this since leaving home.

"This is something for you to celebrate the New Year," intoned Pamuzov, setting a sack next to Father. "Two kilograms flour, half a kilogram refined sugar—not the raw stuff you get from the factory—one kilogram pre-war kasha. And, most importantly, padam! Two splendid chocolate bars. And we ask for nothing in return. Zero. It is a gift for you and the Vorontsevs. Lovely people, wonderful Communists!"

Accepting this bounty would officially make Father a police informant, which he could not allow to happen. "Thank you kindly, but no," he mumbled. The plant manager ushered Father out of the office.

Two days later, the NKVD came to us late in the evening. "Get dressed Yakov Markovitch. Commissar Pamuzov wants to get better acquainted with you."

Petrovna, Mother and the rest of us stared at the policemen with horror in our eyes. The all-too-familiar Soviet nightmare had arrived in Petrovna's hut.

In the morning, Mother walked into the center of Biysk and up the snowy hill to the NKVD compound. The guard would not let her see Father. When she returned home, we uttered a sigh of relief, because Petrovna had feared that Mother would be arrested.

On the fourth day after his imprisonment, Father reappeared on Petrovna's doorstep, half frozen, teeth chattering. Painfully he whispered, "May I please have some fried potatoes?"

We wrapped him in every blanket we had, and Petrovna fried him up a bowl of potatoes. Before he took the first bite, he set us straight. "They wanted me to become an informant, but I refused."

After he was done with the potatoes and uttered a luxurious sigh, Mother unwrapped the blankets, but found no wounds or bruises. "What's that?" she asked, pointing to swollen red blotches.

"Rat bites. During my 'visit,' they used friendly persuasion, tempting me again and again with food and privileges for us and the Vorontsevs. Pamuzov has a file on everyone. When I refused, they threw me into the cellar. "

Petrovna crossed herself. "They say that Our Father the Czar died in a cellar."

There was more. "This cellar was dark and damp. I crawled into a corner and wedged myself in. Then I heard rustling sounds, little feet scurrying. Rats, those gigantic Siberian rats. I willed myself to stay awake, because these famished rats are killers. Later, when I had lost my sense of time, they hauled me out of the cellar and repeated the offer. 'Nyet,' I replied, and it was back to the cellar. I think the rats were delighted to see me. This went on for three days. On the fourth day they hauled me out and said, 'Go home.'"

Father wiped his chin and smiled. "These are the best fried potatoes I have ever eaten."

CHAPTER TWENTY

Being newly minted Soviet citizens, the Poles were informed that they were now *eligible* to be drafted into the Red Army to liberate Mother Russia from the Fascist onslaught.

"Never in the Red Army," the Poles responded and formed their own brigade, connected to their government-in-exile located in London. No one understood how this worked, but somehow it did. Father was in accord for his own reasons. "The fastest way to get killed is in the Red Army. So, I'll throw in my lot with my fellow Poles."

But when he presented himself to the newly formed Polish Military Committee, whose reigning officers were Count Stankiewicz and Mr. Kobielski, the former saddle maker who had been one of the teachers in the ill-fated afternoon school, the Count sneered at Father's request.

"Rubinow, we don't need the likes of you in our midst. A police informer and the man responsible for Father Kwiat's likely death." Father was too proud to remind the Poles that, but for him, they would have disappeared just as the priest had.

Father was not surprised at what came next. On a very cold December night, the NKVD truck pulled up in front of Petrovna's hut and disgorged two local agents. No leather coats, only tunics and green military coats. It snowed outside, nothing out of the ordinary, the clouds shedding lovely white flakes. One of them was an old guy whose belly stretched under his tunic, the second a clean-shaven youngster with freckles.

"Citizen Rubinov," said the older one, "we applaud your desire to fight the Fascists, and the Red Army will help you fulfill it. You have fifteen minutes to pack a bag and say good-bye."

Talk was futile. Father got out of bed and started packing. Mother was frantic. She grabbed the older man by the sleeve. "He is forty-two! Too old to be of any use in the battlefield."

"No one is too old to defend the Motherland."

At that moment Wowka sat up in bed, his eyes glued with sleep. The older NKVD stared at him, then at the gold diploma on the wall. "Ah, smart Jewish boy! Finished high school with all fives. Get out of bed, genius. You're coming with us." Wowka stood up. "Pack your bag, giant. You have an extra ten minutes."

Mother fell on her knees sobbing. "He is too young to fight!" She ran to the table and showed them the certificate of acceptance from Novossibirsk University.

Old NKVD was amused. "Not to worry. The university will find a more deserving Russian to take his place."

I was also out of bed, standing in the corner, dumbfounded. The Vorontsevs were lined up in the doorway.

As Father was ready to step out of the door, Wowka said loudly, "One minute please. Since I am never coming back, there is something my little sister must know." My parents looked uncomfortable. "Ralka, some years before you were born, Mother and I used to spend our summers in the mountains."

"Shut up!" Father screamed, moving toward him.

"Not this time, Papa." Wowka was speaking Russian, not Polish, apparently determined that everyone hear this story. "And there, my mother, then a beautiful Aryan-looking young woman, met young Count Ludwig Zamorski…"

Father jumped at his son, his outstretched hands ready to choke him. The two NKVD men pulled Father away. "Go on with the story. Take your time. This is like an old Russian novel."

Wowka went on: "This lasted for two summers. And it continued in the city when Count Ludwig came to Bialystok whenever he could to meet Mother somewhere secluded. 'When we get married, I'll adopt you,' the Count promised me."

"Lies, all lies!" Father shouted helplessly. "Fira, tell them that he made it all up to humiliate us."

Wowka wouldn't stop. "During the third summer, Mother and Ludwig could not wait any longer. So, when Father came to visit, she asked him for a divorce. And do you know what my hero father did? He called his mother, the great Madame Jadwiga. She came down with her car and chauffer and threatened Mother to disclose the story in Bialystok, which would destroy her parents and the rest of the Rakowski family."

Mother put her hands over her face, moaning. But there was no respite from Wowka.

"And that's how it ended. Mother's punishment for her

adultery was to have another child. And that's you, Ralka. You must have guessed because of the ten years' difference in our ages."

The older NKVD was somber, and the young one confused.

The old man said, "You better shut your mouth, young man." He tore the gold diploma off the wall and shredded it into small pieces.

Without looking back, the NKVD escorted Father and Wowka into the truck.

CHAPTER TWENTY-ONE

Dawn found Mother awake in the bed I shared with her. I heard Petrovna making the usual breakfast preparation noises.

"Svetya, Masha, out of bed!"

My first distinct recollection was that something awful had happened last night. What exactly it was, I couldn't remember. Better think about it after school, when I have more time. This was a new day, or, rather, a repetition of every ordinary day. Mother appeared to be in a stupor, unable to get out of bed.

"Mama, please get up. Petrovna is already making breakfast."

Petrovna stuck her head in the doorway. "Yakovlevna, don't worry. From now on there will be no rent. Your husband and son are Red Army soldiers, and so are my boys." She turned to me. "Don't just stand there, Rala. Get dressed and come eat breakfast."

Sitting behind my desk in school, I made myself forget my troubles by intently studying Olga Maksimovna's poor pink scalp. Almost in front of our eyes she was losing her hair. On top of which she had apparently run out of white bobby pins and had to pin her sparse grey curls with black bobby pins. Awful! I squinted, imagining black insects scurrying on my teacher's raw flesh.

That winter, each day dumped a week's worth of snow, which made it impossible to do my thinking alone outdoors, which I would prefer. Still, I must think. On my return from school I found Mother at the table, staring at an untouched bowl of kasha, the milk still steaming. I ran to her and kissed her. She gave me a pleasant smile.

I knocked on Anushka's door. "Anushka, could I sit in your room for the purpose of thinking?"

She was thrilled by my visit. Anushka was even more beautiful than before, her grief for Dima having chiseled her features into ivory perfection.

"Anushka, did you understand what happened last night?" She nodded. "Wowka said that before I was born, he and Mother spent each summer in the mountains. Right?"

"Absolutely correct."

"Which means that Father sent them." She was listening intently. "And because Father had to work, he visited only on Saturday and Sunday." I was speaking slowly to get my head in order. "When Father was in the city, Mother met a young Polish man who was not a Jew."

"Yes, a Christian."

"And she wanted to go live with him instead of Father. So why did Wowka love the Polish man better than his own father?"

Anushka was crying. "You poor, dear child."

"But my grandmother Jadwiga did not allow this to happen, so they went back to Bialystok. And it was all supposed to remain a secret until Wowka revealed it last night."

"Yes, it's a sad romantic story."

"But what I don't understand is what he said about me. Mama and Papa love me, so how can I be a punishment?"

"Don't think about it, child. He made it all up because he was frightened to go to war and didn't know what he was talking about."

I jumped off the bed and kissed Anushka on both cheeks.

That winter was a million times colder than the last. Three weeks had passed since Father's and Wowka's departure, and still no letters. Mother moved around like a grieving widow, though I didn't know if she grieved equally for Wowka and Father. She did her chores listlessly, lost in her world that had been destroyed too many times.

In the outhouse, the pee and shit froze on impact. It did not stink. because the cold made everything pure and crisp. The town of Biysk sat prettily on the steppe, submerged in whiteness like in a fairytale. The snow remained untouched, forming ice castles as translucent as glass. I was not a sunflower anymore, but a princess flying around on an ice sled.

Each day in class, Olga Maksimovna recited Red Army victories of the previous day. Hundreds of Fascists killed; German planes knocked out of the sky, their tanks smashed to smithereens. At each mention of a Fascist defeat, we clapped enthusiastically.

As the winter strengthened in frost and fury, the school closed. Our hut had turned into an enormous icicle. Svetya, Masha and I spent most of our time in the alcove on top of the stove. We relieved ourselves in a bucket in the corner of the bright room. When the bucket was full, its contents were dumped outside, where they froze before landing.

So here we were, three miserable children with blankets up to our chins. Hungry, dirty and bored, we wondered if this winter would kill us together with our pets, the two nasty, red-haired chickens we named Kukushka and Kokoshka, whom we had saved when the family retreated indoors, leaving the cows, Ruslanka and Ludmila, and another dozen chickens to a certain death.

Life came to a standstill when Marya's truck could not plough through the snow to take her to the hospital. "This season people are dying," Marya said with resignation, "not only from the cold and hunger, but also from infections."

Marya's absence from the hospital plunged us into near starvation. For as long as she went to work, she returned home with food. We knew they were patients' meals, perhaps half- eaten by dying people, some also stolen from the kitchen. Before the truck stopped coming, Marya was the only medical staff; her director, Dr. Kaganov, a refugee from Kiev, was too old to work in this cold. Without the hospital, we rationed the supplies Petrovna had stored for the winter.

This hunger was more frightful than in Old Mud. There, at least we saw the NKVD eat well, so we knew that there was still food in the world. Now, isolated inside a white tower, we were convinced that the entire universe was frozen and dying. We stared at Kukushka and Kokoshka. Will the time come when we we'll have to eat them?

"Eating them would be like cannibalism," Marya said, summing up our thoughts. So, we waited for the snow to melt.

To amuse us, Petrovna recounted every folk story she remembered. So did Marya, but to a lesser degree. Mother recited Pushkin's Eugene Onegin, the same Onegin I had recited at age three, in which Tatiana, who loved Onegin, would not go away with him because she was married to someone else. This made Mother burst into tears, causing me to remember that night more vividly.

One morning we woke up to the realization that we would live. Outside appeared the first subtle signs of a thaw.

"Shall we find Ruslanka and Ludmilla's frozen bodies when the snow melts?" Svetya asked with fear in her voice.

"And all of Kukushka's and Kokoshka's dead cousins," I added.

"I'm sure it'll make me vomit," concluded Masha.

Mother looked around the bright room. "You know what's interesting. There are only females in this house. Adults, children and chickens. It might happen that the world will run out of men."

The mighty water formed by melting snow receded without dragging us down. Sadly, we discovered the carcasses of our cows and chickens, but Marya declared them unfit for human consumption and asked the hospital to remove them. The trucks carried them away. I wondered how many dead cows and horses the trucks had to dispatch somewhere. Throughout the cleanup no one vomited, not even Masha. We released our two chickens to roam freely. They seemed frisky, without a backward look, as happy to be rid of us as were of them.

"It's time we visit the post office," Mother said resolutely. What she did not dare say was that she feared to receive a letter from the Commissar of Military Affairs. But off we went.

The post office hosted a joyful reunion. The women hugged

each other, describing how they had survived the winter. Sadly, some old people had died. They treated each other to roasted pumpkin and sunflower seeds, and, hearts beating wildly, waited for the dreaded letters.

"Yakovlevna, there's a letter for you," said the ancient clerk, waving a triangle with his nicotine-stained fingers.

Mother's hand flew to her heart.

"Mama," I said, "it's a triangle. The government does not write on triangles." She calmed down. By this time in the war, the Soviet Union had run out of envelopes, so people shaped their written pages into a triangle, with the destination in the middle.

It was a letter from Uncle Marek, half of the inside blackened out by the censor.   "Dear family, as you see from the address (Lager 133-B), I am no longer in Kuybishov. Instead I am ... I am translating from English, German, Japanese and Italian. I am here because ... I have two blankets and ... Pigs knuckles are really tasty. Please send rusks. Love, Marek"

I couldn't help wondering, why would they put Uncle Marek in prison? He loves them!"

Mother gave me a rare smile. "Because his time came up."

Years later, Uncle Marek described his downfall in a popular magazine: "I had a very pleasant life in Kuybishov, where all of us Communist intelligentsia took refuge. From there we wrote patriotic propaganda urging our 'valiant troops' to sacrifice themselves for Mother Russia, while we sat in colorful taverns, drinking pre-war vodka and munching on Beluga caviar.

"Everyone was eager to demonstrate to the government that he could contribute something that no one else could. In my case, it was easy. I have a working knowledge of every AXIS language.

I therefore was busy writing leaflets to be dropped to the German troops with such classic threats as, 'Study history, and you'll know that the longer you fight us, the fiercer will be our revenge.' I was especially proud of that one.

"To the Italians, I wrote that Mussolini is a pervert and an idiot and is selling the heroes of Rome and the Renaissance to the vulgar Huns. I am sure that I was the one to suggest that they hang Il Duce upside down.

"But one night, as I sat quietly in my room wearing my new silk robe and smoking a pipe with Prince Albert tobacco, there came a knock. Knocks are bad. I opened the door, and there were two NKVD middle ranks in leather coats. 'Mark Yakovlevich, you are under arrest for spying against the Soviet Union,' they said. In Russian the word for spy is shpion, and if you say it with gusto, your saliva spritzes around.

"I proclaimed my innocence and showed them my documents and decorations.

"'No, you are a shpion,' they shouted, spitting onto their black leather. They proceeded to empty every drawer, then yelled a triumphant 'Aha!' What they had in their grubby hands was my priceless stamp collection, the one I had started as a teenager in Czar Nicolas' jail.

"Oh," I said, relieved. "I am not a shpion. I am a philatelist."

"They rummaged through the album, damaging perfect corners and bending pages. After poking around, they placed their fingers on a German stamp with the likeness of Adolf Hitler, screaming triumphantly 'Shpion!'

"I dressed myself quickly and followed my jailers into the unknown. I never saw Kuybishev again."

CHAPTER TWENTY-TWO

With the warm weather came a frenzy of housecleaning. Buckets of water were mixed with laundry soap and disinfectant that Marya had pinched from the hospital. Scrub brushes reappeared from hiding. Cleanliness meant liberation for Mother and Petrovna.

Another reason to celebrate was a long-awaited letter from Father. "I am not at the front, but working in a blanket factory in… I eat well and am surrounded by old men like me. Kisses, Kuba."

No mail from, or about, Wowka. Excellent! Chances were good that he was still alive.

It was warm enough to fulfill my dream of visiting the public library. I trudged barefoot to the center of Biysk and attempted whistling. No good; tone-deaf people can't whistle.

"Good morning, Comrade Librarian." I had recited the salutation before. "May I please have a book?"

The librarian was supremely happy to see me, and smiled like sunshine at high noon. Her cheeks expanded, and the grey bun on top of her head shone like a divine halo. Was I the first child today asking for a book?

Comrade Librarian ran toward a corner shelf and returned with a book that she placed on the table between us. The name of the book: The Adventures of Tom Sawyer. I hugged "Tom" to my chest. This book would be mine, at least for a short time.

Back home I sat in our bedroom by the window. Mother was elated. "You're reading a book! You are like all the Rakowskis, seeking culture."

Two days later I reappeared in the library and greeted the Comrade Librarian, now my friend Aksinia Nikolaievna, with a curtsy. Her eyes expanded with delight. "Oh, dear God. You curtsied!"

"I love the book you gave, and I want more."

She asked me for my name.

"Rala Yakovlevna," I said. We shook hands, and Aksinia Nikolayevna held it a long time, perhaps to make sure I was real.

"Here is another book by Comrade Mark Tveyn from America. Huckleberry Finn is a friend of Tom Sawyer."

"Oh, good!" I was so happy that I jumped on one foot around her desk.

In the new book people called my hero "Huck," which translates into "Guck" in Russian. So, Guck and his best friend Jim traveled down a river with an impossible name: Mississippi. Must have been a big river to require so many syllables. We in Russia had a very long river with a single syllable. Don.

Two days later I was back in the library, uttering a single word. "More."

Aksynya Nikolaevna's eyes saddened. "I am sorry, Ralichka, but Comrade Tveyn did not write more adventures."

It could not be! Deprivation after ecstasy. I stretched out on the floor and cried, "I want more stories!"

Aksinia knotted her brow. "Yes, of course!" she exclaimed. "I think you may like Comrade Fenimore Cooper, who is also an American and writes stories about white people being cruel to Indians."

I sat down in the library's window seat. Another great story! In my book, called The Last of the Mohicans, white people who wear big hats and carry guns fight Indians who run around half-naked, but with feathers in their hair. Most astonishing are the white ladies, all of them beautiful and blond, and each of them at some point in the story is saved by a man in a hat. From the illustration, it was clear that America is a country where all the fighting stops in the end of a book, and everyone lives happily ever after. Though I wasn't sure about the Indians.

In the next weeks I read so much that I soon earned another benefit. Each time, upon my arrival, Aksinia Nikolayevna treated me to a glass of milk and a sugar cookie.

There is no more cultured place in the world than a library!

CHAPTER TWENTY-THREE

I t was summertime, but we were still hungry. After the past winter, all of us students and our teacher Olga Maksimovna, looked thinner than the previous year. One evening, Petrovna shocked us with a round loaf of bread she proudly displayed in the middle of our dining room table. We touched it. It was real, a whole round loaf, just for us. Petrovna cut the bread in half, and one half into seven slices, handing a slice to each of us. She wrapped the uncut half in a cloth and put it away.

How could Petrovna afford to bake the bread? The answer: after my mother had renounced her brasserie trade, she and Petrovna put their savings away under the mattress, next to the Bible. With it they bought a ten-kilogram sack of flour on the black market.

"From now on we shall have a fresh loaf once a week," Petrovna assured us.

Svetya asked the question all of us children wondered about. "Grandma, what is the black market, and where is it located?"

This was such a funny question that the adults laughed

heartily. Marya tried to explain. "The market is 'black' because you cannot see it. It is made up of whispers about sellers who have things in their homes, so people go there to buy. We have to do this because there are no stores in the Soviet Union."

Later, Svetya, Masha and I sat on the stoop.

I said, "You know how Nadya said in school that her mother earns money by selling bread rolls made of zmykh to soldiers in the garrison?"

Masha pretended to vomit. Rightly so, because zmykh was cow manure mixed with earth and straw, stomped on by bare feet and poured into square pans that were left in the sun to harden. Once firm, these cow-shit bricks were used to construct fences or broken up into smaller pieces and fed back to the cows, which would make me vomit if I were a cow. Even more disgusting was to feed this to real people.

Disgusting or not, we decided to go into the zmykh-baking business. First, we had to obtain the raw material from somewhere in town, because without a cow, we were zmykh-less. That done, we needed a mortar and pestle to pulverize it into a flour-like consistency. Next, we had to mix it with some real flour stolen from Petrovna's cache and bake everything into a pancake called lepeshkis, which means shapeless pieces of bread.

"And salt," Svetya remembered.

"Isn't it a sin what we're doing?" asked Masha, which shut us up for a while.

"Well—maybe not," I said at last, "because we don't intend to keep the money. We'll give it to Petrovna and my mother to use for everyone."

Svetya nodded. "Maybe they will buy a chicken we can roast."

Kukushka and Kokoshka were still alive, and we intended to do them no harm.

We stole two blocks of zmykh from a truck in the town center, dragged it home, and stored it in the abandoned cowshed. We needed an adult to help us in this enterprise, and picked Anushka. So how did we persuade this righteous lady to bake the pancakes?

Svetya: "We'll promise that the money will go toward buying a cow."

Hearing this, Anushka clapped her hands. "Oh, yes!"

Anushka gathered the ingredients and disappeared. The next day she returned with six lepeshkis, two for each to carry. They resembled normal rolls, but we shuddered to think how they tasted.

After school we headed for the fence surrounding the Red Army garrison. There we dispersed, lepeshkis in our apron pockets. Smiling, I approached my part of the fence. I wasn't alone. Other people milled around selling sunflower and pumpkin seeds. There were also a couple of pretty older girls in short skirts, but I didn't know what they were selling.

"Twenty kopeks!" I addressed a red belt buckle, which was all I could see of the soldier behind the barbed wire. A hand with dirty fingernails handed me thirty.

"Thirty," I told a soldier further down the line. I got twenty-five. That hurt, because I had already imagined myself a successful capitalist.

All in all, Svetya, Masha and I were raking in money. We practiced looking needy, but also attractive, a method that doubled and tripled our earnings. Anushka gave us a lidded jar for the money, which she marked: "For the cow."

People at the fence looked happier, secure in the belief that soon we would win the war. More pretty, older girls were attracted to the fence. Best of all, we had not heard that anyone had died after consuming our baked goods.

The day I asked a soldier for fifty kopeks, he unbuttoned his pants and peed on me. The stupid muzhik! Svetya, Masha and I ran to the brook, where we took off our clothes and submerged ourselves in cold water. I rinsed my clothes and returned home wet. Thank God I didn't die of pneumonia. The next day, to spite the imbecile soldier, I asked, and received, sixty kopeks.

Trade was brisk, and the "cow jar" almost full. So, what could go wrong?

My big mouth, of course. One afternoon I broke a self-imposed rule not to conduct conversations with the soldiers. So here I was at the gate, showing a soldier my lepeshkis, when he said, "What's your name, child?" When he gave me a whole ruble, I noticed that his hands were hairier than most. I stuck the money in my apron pocket and looked up to thank him. He was older, with curly brown hair and lots of silver.

I felt sorry for him. "My name is Rala."

"Such a pretty name. I have a daughter your age. Here is her picture."

She was a thin girl with black pigtails and fuzzy eyes. "She's very nice," I said, and handed him back the photo.

"She is a little Jewish girl, like you."

"Why do you think I'm Jewish? Maybe I'm a Gypsy."

"It's your eyes." Eyes were eyes. I had no idea what he meant.

"How is life in Biysk?" he asked.

I knew the answer. "Great, excellent."

"And how was it home in Poland?"

"Oh, it was wonderful."

Too late! I said what I shouldn't have! I looked at the soldier and saw him smiling with satisfaction. He tricked me, and now he'll denounce me. And my mother. We shall all go to jail, even the Vorontsevs.

I told the girls not to ask questions, but to run home with me.

"We are in trouble," I told Mother and Petrovna, as soon as we stepped through the door.

They stared at us, uncomprehending. From the corner of my eye, I saw Anushka creeping outdoors. I talked fast, eager to get it over with. "I told a soldier at the garrison fence that life in Poland was wonderful."

"And what were you doing at the fence?" Petrovna demanded.

We looked at each other. Masha began to cry. Svetya and I explained our brilliant scheme and financial success. To our disappointment, all the women said was, "You fed zmykh to human beings?"

"Everyone does it," Svetya and I said together.

Petrovna hit Svetya across the face. "Not everyone does it! And this is not the excuse of an honorable person."

Mother began, "If your father were here—" then stopped. It was the first time since that night that she had mentioned Father.

Anushka walked in with the jar and admitted her part in the conspiracy. She dumped the money on the table. It was a larger pile than we had anticipated. A tiny smile hovered in the corner of Petrovna's mouth. Recovering her composure, she put the money into a sack and shoved it under her mattress.

For the next two weeks, while eating, we stared at Petrovna's mattress. When Marya learned of our transgression, she grinned. "What's done is done. There's no one you can return the money to."

Petrovna hesitated. "But God may punish us."

"God is on vacation. He went to Sochi to ski. Time to use the money."

We were relieved.

Anushka, Petrovna and Mother went out and brought back a cow. We called her Victoria, but couldn't figure out how you buy a cow on the black market.

CHAPTER TWENTY-FOUR

One summer day, the sun refused to move off the middle of the sky. Everyone at home was engaged in something useful. Svetya and Masha were helping their grandmother prepare meatballs from the one half kilogram of beef she had bought on the black market. A lot of bread was needed to stretch the beef to feed seven people.

It was inevitable that soon I would be called in to help. But the day was too beautiful to waste on meatballs. As fast as an arrow, sprinted out of the house and plunged into the sunflower field, so high that it could not be seen from the road. For a while I ran at a steady pace, and when I stopped and looked back, the hut was no longer visible. Suddenly I heard the muffled noise of an approaching truck. I spread the sunflowers apart and looked onto the road. Twirling in the distance was a pillar of dust. My heart stopped. In Biysk an approaching truck means that someone you love is in trouble. But I was also curious, and moved closer. The dust had thinned to reveal an army truck, its wheels tinted white.

Noticing me, the driver slowed down, then stopped. A man came out of the passenger door and stood by the side of the road, his eyes focusing on a plump sunflower, his fingers running over the black seeds. Even more curious now, I approached him slowly. He could not hear me because I was barefoot and walking on tippy toes. But he must have sensed something, because he lifted his eyes and saw me gawking.

"Who the hell are you?" he snapped.

He was a cripple. His right pegleg made him look like the man in Treasure Island, a book I had just read. The pegleg was fastened to his knee with a leather belt. His good left leg wore a muddy boot.

The driver stared at us staring at each other. The cripple was tall and thin, so thin that his army belt was tied at his waist, instead of buckled. "Kid, you never saw a pegleg?"

"No," I answered, and he burst out laughing. In a better mood now, he introduced himself. "Dimitry Stepanovich Vorontsev, returning from the Great Patriotic War."

Impossible! This man is a ghost! After all, Mother and I were the first to learn that Dima was dead. I must warn everyone. Not looking at him, I turned around and ran across the field, cutting through the sunflowers. While running, I glimpsed the truck winding its way to Petrovna's house.

I slowed from a run to a steady pace. Arriving in the courtyard, I expected to hear sounds of joy from within. But there was silence. The sun's orange ball was waddling precariously over our home, its rays hitting the roof.

I straightened my dress and walked into the bright room. There he was, not a ghost. So why did the women behave as if he was? Scattered around the room, they watched as Dima sat at the dining table in front of a steaming bowl of kasha. His eyes were half- closed, exhibiting an incredible tiredness. The unstrapped pegleg lay on the floor. Obviously pinching him, it must have been the first thing he had discarded. Now relaxed, he bore some resemblance to the wedding picture of him and Anushka that I had seen in their bedroom.

Why wasn't Anushka kissing and hugging her husband? Instead, she looked terrified.

Dima saw me in the room. "Ah, a friendly face. Is this your daughter, Yakovlevna?"

Sveyia and Masha grabbed me, and we ran outside.

"Anushka said he used to be a great dancer," Svetya remembered.

"Is he a hero because he lost his leg fighting the Fascists?" Masha wondered.

We looked at each other, undecided.

"Maybe yes," Svetya said. "A man who lost a leg fighting Nazis deserves to be called a hero."

I was still curious. "What did Anushka do when he walked through the door?"

"She fainted," Svetya smiled, "and the others looked like they were going to faint."

"So how long did she stay on the floor in a fainting condition?"

"Not long, because Grandma poured cold water on her face."

"Oh, dear Lord," I said. I had learned this phrase from the librarian, and saying it made me feel Russian.

Svetya, Masha and I became obsessed with what would happen between Dima and Anushka. For us it was a fairytale about a beautiful maiden and a handsome, if slightly damaged, hero. We listened through the thin walls, were shooed away by Petrovna, and peered through the window, all of it done with impolite curiosity.

Here are some results of our eavesdropping.

Anushka to Dima: "I'm so happy you're alive!"

Dima to Anushka: "Thank you."

Anushka: "How long did they keep you in the hospital?"

Dima: "Four months."

We jumped off the windowsill. Svetya said she would ask her mother if a patient ever stayed four months in her hospital. At the end of a week, we could attest that the couple did not "do it."

Our next information source was Victoria the Cow, to whom Anushka was known to confess. Here's a sample: "Maybe he doesn't want to kiss me because I fainted when I saw him." We nodded, as did the cow. "Oh, how wonderful Dima used to be! So handsome and the best dancer in Biysk." Anushka cried. Victoria, apparently tired of her mistress's complaints, resumed chewing.

The following week, we noticed that Dima was returning to being a little handsomer, as if his young self was peeking through his suffering. He shaved his stubbly beard and dressed in his old civilian clothes, but they had to cut off the left trouser to fit the pegleg.

The question of Dima's heroism remained unanswered. One time I snuck into Anushka's and Dima's room, found his green rucksack, and in it a cloth bag full of medals. I tried to memorize what some of them looked like. In the library I drew a picture of several medals and showed them to Aksinya Nikolayevna.

"These three," she pointed to a star, a flag, and a picture of Lenin and Stalin, "are the most important. For bravery above and beyond the call of duty. Whose are they?"

"A man who was supposed to be dead, but is alive." I said. "He returned home with a wooden leg and is very sad."

"Yes, child," said Raisa Alexandrovna, a second librarian. "We live in sad times and in a sad land."

Back home I found Dima and Anushka looking happy. "I need to put another hole in this bloody belt," Dima was saying. "Anushka, bring me a nail so I can punch another hole."

Anushka smiled. "No need, Dimochka. We will give you such good food you will not need another hole."

Without warning, Dima slammed his fist into the table. "Why do you women think that all the world's troubles can be cured with a bowl of kasha?"

Later that night Svetya, Masha and I were on the Dima Watch. There were some noises from their bedroom. Then came Anushka's soft voice. "Dima, would you let me see your knee?"

"Trust me, you don't want to see it. It's too ugly. That surgeon was a butcher, on top of which he was drunk."

Pause. No sound, no rustle. Clearly, he did not let his wife see his knee. We almost jumped off, but there was more. Anushka dared again. "How did it happen?"

And that's when he totally blew up. "I am not going to entertain you, or any of the others, with war stories. What happened happened, and I don't want to talk about it!"

He opened the bedroom door, slammed it behind him, and walked into the field.

In the morning Svetya, Masha and I watched as Anushka milked Victoria. Dima came out of the house, smiling broadly. He waved to us and addressed his wife.

"You look especially beautiful this morning, Anushka."

"You don't look so bad yourself, Dimochka."

CHAPTER TWENTY-FIVE

Anushka and Dima seemed unable to settle into a life together, because he would erupt unpredictably into moods no one could understand or prevent. Fear spread throughout the house. Petrovna was afraid, not knowing how much his character, damaged by war, might turn explosive. Marya resented Dima returning home, when the family and the world in general would have been better served if the one returning were her husband, Borya. My mother was afraid that somehow Dima's present would force Petrovna to send us away, in which case we would probably die.

One afternoon, Mother and I were alone in the house, where she was reading to me Krilov's tale about an industrious ant and a lazy cricket. Dima suddenly walked into the bright room. "You have a beautiful voice, Yakovlevna. You are Jews, right? I can tell, because Rala has Jewish eyes."

Mother chuckled. "There is no such thing as Jewish eyes. It's a Christian invention." She closed the book and grabbed her heavy woolen shawl, because the weather was signaling the oncoming frost.

Dima asked where we were headed.

"To the post office," Mother answered, and he volunteered to escort us.

The post office was more than a kilometer away, and we were impressed with how well Dima had learned to walk on his piece of wood. When we arrived, Mother went over to Efim the clerk, and Dima leaned heavily against the wall, switching his weight to his healthy leg. Efim was rolling himself a cigarette, evenly distributing a pinch of tobacco along a neatly cut square of Pravda.

He noticed Dima and asked, "Want a smoke?"

Dima nodded, fetching paper and tobacco from Efim and impatiently rolling for himself a thick uneven cigarette. When it was lit, he puffed so greedily that I thought he might spit out burning ashes.

Through Dima's smoke, I noticed Mother put a letter in her pocket. Mother and I thought that Dima was too busy smoking to notice our letter. But he saw it, and, once outside, told Mother, "Read your letter, Yakovlevna." There was something in his voice that made her obey.

"Dear Mama and Rala," she read aloud. Thank God, Wowka was still alive. "We have an excellent commanding officers and the food is good." Dima laughed. When she came to the final sentence, "Our goal is right, we shall be victorious," Dima's laughter turned into a roar.

Mother told me to walk ahead, which meant that she would walk alongside Dima to catch him if he stumbled in the dark. Shortly, a shadow detached itself from behind a tree and grabbed me by the throat.

"Cripple, give me your army food rations. And I want your

wife's jewelry or I'll kill your kid, I swear." Dima leaned against Mother for support. "Fast!" shouted the attacker. "I belong to the Black Cats. See for yourself." The hooligan brandished a black glove, into which, as everyone in Biysk knew, were sewn sharp claws. He jabbed me in the neck, and I yelped.

Suddenly, Dima pounced on the hooligan and pulled him off me. A switchblade shone in Dima's hand, its sharp long blade gleaming wickedly in the night. The knife ripped through the attacker's shirt, pressing against his bare chest. He was a boy, with a little speck of beard showing, a disgusting boy, the kind that attacked me the previous summer.

Dima let go a stream of curses, the vileness of which I had never heard before. Then he stood the boy up and ran the knife twice across his chest, which immediately turned red. "Give me your famous glove." Dima grabbed the black glove and shoved it in his pocket. "Next time I see you around here, I'll kill you."

The hooligan ran. Mother and I stood there, shivering. Dima wiped his switchblade and stuck it behind his boot. "Trust me, Yakovlevna. I shall never allow anything bad to happen to you or your kid."

Then he went on ahead, whistling a dance tune.

In the following days, we managed to visit the post office without Dima. One day brought a delightful surprise: a letter from my aunt Zila in Palestine. It had travelled far and wide, through a city called Tehran, which, Mother explained, was in the ancient kingdom of Persia, Palestine's neighbor. The good news was that Zila and David were happy and healthy, but without children. Mina was married to an engineer, but the two were also childless.

Father's sister Sonya and her husband Miron had a son.

"My answer to Zila will be the height of diplomacy," Mother said.

"What's diplomacy?" I asked

"Let me think. Diplomacy is when your government sends you abroad to lie for your country, and you manage to lie with a smiling, honest face."

I laughed and kicked pebbles. Since we were now co-conspirators, the next day Mother showed me her "diplomatic" letter. "My dear sisters Zila and Mina, we are all happy living in Biysk. This happiness is because everyone hear gets the same portion of food. We live with a wonderful family, who are prime examples of the great Russian soul."

"But it's true about their soul, so where is the diplomacy?"

"Yes, when a Russian writes how well he eats, it means that he is hungry. Listen to the rest of it: 'I have a patch of soil where I grow my own potatoes. It is far from our house, but I love the brisk walk. Wowka and Kuba are away fighting the Fascists, and everyone is proud of them. Our goal is righteous—we shall be victorious!"

CHAPTER TWENTY-SIX

After Dima saved me from the hooligan at the post office, I considered him an exciting and dangerous hero. Still, I was happy to return to school, far away from his dark moods and outbursts.

Our teacher, Olga Maksimovna, had less hair and more pink blotches on her scalp. But we Vorontsev girls looked better than we had last year. Petrovna had sewn for us fancy gingham aprons.

"When the war is over, I'll make for each of you new dresses," she promised. I was hoping for a pair of real shoes, because all summer we walked barefoot, putting on our tapochkis—home-sewn moccasins—only in school or when visiting people who matter.

School was screamingly boring. In the morning, our Education Commissar delivered a lecture to all grades praising Comrade Stalin and the Great Patriotic War. In class, we were supposed to sit straight, hands on desks, palms down. If a question was asked and you knew the answer, you put your right elbow on the desk, arm straight, waiting for the teacher to recognize you.

On the third day of school, a yawn forced its way out of my mouth. Not a small dainty yawn, but a monstrous, ogre-like yawn. Everyone stared at me. Even I stared at me, never having yawned so thunderously before.

"Rala, Communist children don't yawn in class," Olga Maksimovna hissed through her gapped teeth.

"I am so sorry, Olga Maksimovna, but our cow Victoria was sick all night and moaning, so I couldn't fall asleep."

"So why is Svetya fresh and alert?"

Svetya to the rescue.   "Olga Maksimovna, Victoria wasn't moaning under our window, but under Rala's."

On the way home Svetya said, "Better behave, or the next time, she'll hit you with the ruler."

One day on our way back home from school, Svetya, Masha and I encountered a throng of very old people gathered around an ancient hut. They were smiling, as if something nice had happened to them. Christian prayers were heard from within, the kind Petrovna often murmured. But it was not the chanting that pulled us over, but the delicious smell of food wafting through the air.

We had chanced upon a pominki, a wake, an event where food miraculously appeared in these days of semi-hunger. Petrovna had explained the bounty to us. "The dead must be surrounded by food on their final journey. Even though they might have been hungry on Earth, they will remember food when they arrive in Paradise."

"In peace let us pray to the Lord," intoned a gaunt prayer

leader.

"Lord have mercy," chanted the congregation. Svetya, Masha and I were especially vocal in our singing.

The food was arranged on a table behind the dead man's head. An old woman stood beside him gumming a cabbage roll stuffed with bread and some meat. On a platter were dumplings filled with mashed potatoes and fried onions. We grabbed as much food as we could hold and ducked under the table on which the corpse was laid out. We ate enthusiastically, finishing everything.

As we climbed out from under the table, a veiny hand patted our heads. "You poor orphans."

We were not about to argue that we were not complete orphans, because everyone in this land, in one way or another, was an orphan. We were about to sneak out of the hut, when the old lady, who appeared to be the widow, handed us a package of food wrapped in gauze. "For your mothers."

Svetya and Masha crossed themselves. So did I.

The warm weather was bidding us good-bye. The sun meandered gently through the tree tops, lazy and irresponsible. I ran down to the brook for a special farewell to summer. The path was downhill, the steepest part near the water. As I emerged onto the bank, I saw Dima sitting on a rock, playing the harmonica. Sunshine turned the brook's glossy surface into a golden shimmer. Like all Russian songs, this one was about someone's going away and dying.

"God afternoon, malinkya!" Recently he had given me this name, which in Russian means "little one."

Civilian clothes looked good on him, especially his new black leather belt.

"Dima, you look better than the first day I saw you."

"You will grow up to be a terrific flirt, malinkaya."

Definitely a compliment.

"Do you know how to play the tune from the movie 'Sun Valley Serenade'?"

I tried not to think about the girl in the yellow dress who was murdered the night I had seen it. But the tune lingered in my mind.

"Ah, the American movie. The doctors in the hospital told me that the Americans could give me a leg that looks real. Maybe you and I can go to America together?"

Dima played, and we sang together. Me badly.

When December turns into May

In this lovely season,

For no special reason

My heart turns to you.

He shoved the harmonica into his boot and took out the switchblade. I shuddered, backing away. He noticed, but said nothing. He reached for a piece of driftwood.   "Would you like me to make you a clown?"

I nodded. Dima chiseled carefully, his fingers as elegant as when he played the harmonica. The final motion was pecking out the clown's eyes. "Padam!" he exclaimed.

The clown was a disappointment. Who needs a sad clown

with a crooked grin? On top of which Dima made him cry, with two fat teardrops pouring down his cheeks.

He spat looking at his clown.   "I did not mean for him to come out so ugly. You know what, I shall chisel you a beautiful doll and a happy clown, so next spring you can swim with them in this brook."

"Oh, thank you! But I don't think we'll be here next spring. The war will be over, and we'll return home."

For some reason this made him angry. "You don't want to go back to Poland, malinkaya. Trust me, there is no one left over there alive. You'll be much happier staying here."

"No, you're a liar, a big fat liar! I have a very big family there, and they are all alive!"

Dima grabbed me by the shoulders.   "Malinkaya,   you and your mother must wake up to the truth. Everyone you left back home was killed by Fascists."

I threw the miserable clown at him and ran up the hill. With tremendous effort he caught up with me. "I made it all up. I swear! I don't know why the Devil makes me hurt people. Please, trust me, everyone is alive. Everything I told you is a lie."

On Sunday, Dima knocked on our door with a bouquet of wildflowers wrapped in a sheet of Pravda. By now, I had accepted his word that he had made up the terrible story, and I did not talk about it with Mother.

Dima gave Mother his flowers. "People in town say that around this time is your Jewish New Year. So happy New Year, Yakovlevna and Rala."

Mother thanked him. Then silence. Remembering her

manners, she invited him to sit with us. He declined and remained standing.

"They say that you are an ancient people. So what year is it?"

"I don't know. At home, my father told us about it." Mother smiled, and Dima returned her smile.

On Sunday night, after a day in town, Dima returned home drunk—so drunk that he could not find his own door. Undecided, he stood outside, shaking on his pegleg and weaving unsteadily. He was yelling something, like a dog barking at the moon.

"Samogon," Petrovna whispered. Even we kids knew that the word stood for bad home-brewed vodka. Men in town drank it, and even some women. It was as deadly as tuberculosis. Real vodka was available for the NKVD and the high-ranking staff at the Red Army garrison. The others drank samogon, with, according to rumors, ingredients such as rubbing alcohol, potato peels, roots of anything that grew, or whatever else an imaginative brewer would pour into it.

Dima shuffled outside our window. He looked up and shouted, "Come out, you miserable Jewish bitch! You and your bastard!"

Mother took me in her arms. By now everyone was awake. Petrovna pulled Mother and me away from the window. Below, Dima ran around in circles, belching and shouting curses. Then he threw a stone into our window, shattering the glass.

Petrovna got ahold of her heavy frying pan and headed to our room. Dima must have found his way to the cowshed and brought out a ladder. He anchored it onto the wall and began climbing. "Mama," he yelled, "you must throw out the Jewess. She will bring us bad luck! She and her kid must go! Believe me, Jews are bloodsuckers!"

Sitting in the bright room, we noticed his head peeking through the shattered glass. He grabbed the window frame and cut himself. He screamed and fell backward, the ladder on top of him. As if not realizing that he was bleeding, Dima picked up the ladder once more and leaned it against our window. Climbing up with blood on his hands, he mumbled incoherently. When his head popped in again, Petrovna hit him with the frying pan. He and the ladder crashed into the ground.

Petrovna, Marya and Anushka ran outside and dragged Dima into his own room. Anushka tried to clean him up, but Petrovna stopped her. "No point doing it now. Let him sleep it off. Tonight everyone sleeps in the bright room."

Svetya, Masha and I climbed on top of the furnace.

In the morning, when Anushka went to check on her husband, he was gone.

CHAPTER TWENTY-SEVEN

Dima had been gone for more than a week, and calm returned to the Vorontsev household. In the evenings, Svetya and I read to Petrovna forbidden Bible stories. She liked the one in which Jesus turned water into wine, and another about feeding a multitude with five loaves and five fishes. Petrovna was amused.

"Oh, Jesus, if you could only perform this miracle in Biysk."

Marya brought a workman from the hospital who replaced the glass on our broken window. Just in time, because cold winds were gathering into a storm.

In the intensifying cold, a miraculous package arrived from Palestine via the magical city of Tehran. Zila and Mina had sent men's pants, sweaters and shirts, woolen socks and mittens, and a checkered man's scarf. Dresses for the ladies, also wool sweaters and dresses in different sizes for us little ladies.

I laughed, "Mama, now I know what you meant by 'diplomacy.'"

"How much of the men's clothing do we sell, and how much do we save for Dima?" Mother asked.

"We must keep the women's and girls' clothing," was Petrovna's verdict. "And sell the rest."

Mother picked up the scarf. "For Kuba."

I hoped no one saw me lifting a pair of men's socks for Dima, if he ever returned. But how do you gift a pair of socks to a one-legged man?

Once again winter arrived, laden with snow. But that winter, 1944, was not as bad as the last. Schools remained open, and we were not reduced to sleeping with the chickens.

In school, Olga Maksimovna was explaining the concept of rape. "When the Mongol hordes invaded Russia, they burned the villages, killed the men, and raped the women. When the White Russians stormed the Don, they burned the villages, killed the men, and raped the women. Now the Fascists are burning the villages, killing the men, and raping the women..."

Dima had been absent for a very long time. Anushka and the rest of us continued living in peace, as if Dima had never returned from the war, or had not been part of our lives for a short time. The only thing Mother and I knew, but did not tell Petrovna, was that a woman at the post office gossiped that Dima Vorontsev had been sighted in the company of "drunks, hooligans and fallen women."

"Mama, what's a fallen woman, and where did she fall?"

"Well, she fell from good behavior into bad behavior."

"So, when I behave badly, I become a fallen woman?"

"No, you become a misbehaving child."

We received another parcel of clothing from Palestine and, without debate, sold everything on the black market. At this point the townspeople seemed to have more money, and trade was brisk. Unfortunately, no more letters arrived from Uncle Marek, not even to thank us for the rusks.

"No point sending more rusks to a man who might be dead," concluded Marya, perhaps because in the past we had eaten so many meals of dead people.

It was three years now since we had been brought here from Bialystok, and over a year since Father and Wowka had been taken away. I was already eight-and-a-half and had read so many books that I stopped counting. Mother switched from reading Pushkin and Krilov to another famous poet, Vlodimir Lermontov, who wrote a poem called "Borodino," in which the Russians defeat Napoleon Bonaparte, a Frenchman stupid enough to invade Russia.

"Hitler should have read Lermontov," Mother remarked.

Again, winter bloomed into spring; still no Dima. Still, from time to time, I would go down to the brook, hoping. One day, there he was, sitting on his usual rock, whistling and whittling a piece of driftwood. By now I knew enough about drunks to recognize that Dima was sober. He was clean-shaven and dressed in brown pants and a striped shirt.

Without looking, he said. "I knew you would come, malinkaya."

"You look nice," I said, sitting next to him on the rock.

"Such a flirt you are. But thanks anyway." Another compliment.

"Mother and I heard at the post office that you live with hooligans and fallen women."

He roared with laughter. "When this war is over, every man

in Russia will be bad. And with what happened to us, we deserve to enjoy our badness. Now, about women. There are two kinds of ladies in this world: the good ones, like our mothers, who cook and worry. Then there are those who do not cook or worry." He winked. "Those are wonderful and desirable."

"Dima, last summer you promised to tell me how you lost your leg."

"I lost my leg stepping on a mine. You see, the Fascists surprised us in 1941. Your family knows it better than anyone. Our soldiers were badly trained, had few weapons, trucks or airplanes. And no minesweepers. Do you know what's a minesweeper?"

"Maybe like a big tractor?"

"Close enough. These machines, unmanned, are sent into the field to blow up the mines. Boom, boom, boom! Then the infantry marches on a cleared field. But with the Red Army, we the soldiers, were turned into minesweepers. They sent us by the thousands to walk through the mines and blow ourselves up. Somehow I survived."

I was sobbing, and Dima consoled me. "You must be strong, malinkaya. There is so much evil in the world."

One night, in October, when the ground was already covered with snow, my father returned home. The cracking snow and ice woke us up. We listened, hearts pounding, as footsteps approached. The first thought was: the NKVD. The next thought: hooligans, equally bad. Thankfully, Father was smart enough to shout before he stepped onto the porch.

"It's me, Kuba Rubinov, returning from the war! Don't be scared!"

We were stunned with joy. Mother and I ran to the door, and there he was, shaking snow off his soldier's coat.

Instinctively, Petrovna ran to the stove and began frying potatoes.

Mother and I kissed and hugged him, keeping the terrible scene of his departure in the backs of our minds and hoping that he would do the same.

Father sniffed the aroma coming from the kitchen. Petrovna kept frying, but Marya, Anushka and we girls crowded around him and touched him, as if fearing that he might melt into a puddle on the floor. After Father ate a colossal portion of fried potatoes, he slept for ten hours. When he woke up, we were treated to his war story.

"Not very exciting, I warn you. At the selection point, they separated the young and the old." Mother lowered her eyes, realizing that Father did not mention Wowka's name. "We oldsters traveled by train to Novossibirsk, where they sent me to a blanket depot. We arranged those blankets that soldiers carry around their chests. "

"You were so near?" Mother puzzled. The end of that question should have been: So why didn't you write more? But of course, we knew the answer.

Father was nearing the end of his tale. "But then I got very sick with anemia and malnutrition, a common ailment in the army. That's when they decided that it would be cheaper to send me home than keep me in the hospital."

After a week of nourishing food and extraordinary care, Father marched off to the sugar beet factory and was reinstated in his former position. At payday, he received his first bundle of rubles, with which he bought half a kilogram of beef on the black market. The last time I saw so much meat was in 1943, when we were in the business of selling pancakes made of cow manure to Red Army fighters.

"This is for the whole family," Father announced proudly.

3"Absolutely not," countered Petrovna. "The three of you must eat it alone, in your room, as a family."

Mother cooked the meat in a covered pot, then added kasha and carrots. She spooned out the largest portion for Father, because he had supplied us with meat. We brought in an additional chair from the bright room and ate our meal at the little table by the window, chewing happily and looking at each other.

In the middle of the meal, Father walked over to me and ruffled my hair.

"Eat, child, eat." I had never seen him more proud.

CHAPTER TWENTY-EIGHT

O ur goal is righteous, and we have won the war!

For us Polish deportees, victory, as sweet as it was, ushered in fear and anxiety. What would happen to us?

Father explained the political situation: The victorious leaders, Churchill, Roosevelt and Stalin, were meeting in a city called Yalta, and debating what to do with the world now that the war was over.

"They discuss the fate of nations like moving chess pieces on a board." Father said. "You take this, but I absolutely need this, however I can swap you this country for the one more to the east."

We laughed, as a Yiddish expression goes, "with lizards." After all, we were but pawns on the chessboard of the world.

Victory over the Nazis inspired Mother toward thoughts about my future. While peeling potatoes for supper, she said, "I must teach you good manners."

"We don't need good manners in the Soviet Union."

"People need good manners wherever they are. But especially back home in Bialystok among sophisticated people, young ladies must display style and grace. And they must know a little French. It's a wonderful code of behavior called etiquette."

"Before I learn this etiquette, I want to read all the great books in the world."

"Darling, one thing has nothing to do with the other. As Pushkin said, you may be an honorable person and get a manicure every week. It won't hurt if you learn to peel an orange the right way."

"What's an orange?"

Only one item of the Yalta debates concerned us personally: Who gets Poland? One day a deal was made, and Father brought home the happy news. "Poland will again become independent, with Bialystok in it. We, as Polish citizens, will be returned to our birthplace. The decree applies not only to us in Biysk, but to Polish citizens serving in the Red Army."

"Oh, my God, Wowka will be allowed to come home!" Mother hugged me.

The Yalta Rules, as they were called, brought happiness to the deportees. At first, every Rubinow hugged and kissed every Vorontsev. I kissed and hugged Svetya and Masha. When we realized that our freedom meant that we might not see each other again, we began to cry.

Petrovna put a stop to it. "It's God's will." She took the Bible from under her mattress. "Svetya, read to me the story about Jews leaving Egypt and going back to their country."

One day, soon after school began in the autumn of 1945, as Svetya, Masha and I came out of school, we saw the biggest mob of people lining the street, quietly staring at men marching in the middle. We pushed ourselves closer. Dozens, maybe hundreds, maybe more little men, really small and thin in grey uniforms we had never seen before, were marching through Biysk.

Then we heard people whispering, Japanese prisoners of war. Japanese prisoners of war in Biysk? More and more coming from somewhere, marching through Biysk. Svetya, Masha and I said in unison, "Old Mud."

I was the only one who knew the place. "But it's not big enough."

Svetya had an answer. "There many places like Old Mud in Siberia."

Back home we told the family about what we had seen.

"Yes," Marya said. "We fought a war with Japan, and this time we won."

Mother said dreamily, "My brother Marek translated the Japanese folktales into Yiddish."

Life continued, varying between happy and sad. An emotional problem for me to solve was, since we had always wanted deep in our hearts to leave this place, why were we now sad to the point of giving it up and staying here? The more I battled this idea, the more I realized that there was no answer.

Mother and Father were holding hands for the first time since his return. Perhaps, after all, one Polish Count could not ruin the rest of their lives.

Throughout everything, Wowka was stationed with the Red Army in Germany. His letters were jubilant. Russian soldiers grabbed everything they wanted; nothing was off limits; they were kings and lords after what they had suffered in the war. The Germans were cowards in their defeat.

"Finally I have a great life," Wowka stated in one letter.

But his next letter was shocking. "Dear parents and Ralka," he wrote. "I hope you will understand my decision to renounce my Polish citizenship. I have a wonderful life here in Germany with the Soviet occupation forces. We have been assured that we shall stay here for decades. I deserve a good life, as I have fought and suffered from Stalingrad to Berlin. I wish you three the best of happiness back in Bialystok. Your son, Wowka."

Father threw his arms up in the air. "No one has ever renounced an opportunity to get out of the Soviet Union. This is the height of stupidity and recklessness."

It might have been, though I wondered if deep in his heart, Father was not pleased to never again have to deal with his son.

The end of the war brought Dima back home, carrying gifts: dresses for the ladies, two for Anushka, socks and ribbons for Svetya, Masha and me. He and Anushka kissed the way they should have kissed when he first came back from the war. Petrovna cried with joy. I thought that after this, we should all take a vacation from tears.

I wondered what to do with the Palestinian socks that I had kept for Dima. I couldn't give them to him, not even in our happy mood. Quietly, I slipped the socks into Father's rucksack.

In March, 1946, the Soviet authorities finally processed the papers necessary to take us back to Bialystok. Dima had been home with Anushka for almost a year. He bought his wife another cow, and they named her Anushka Two. I wondered what names they would give their children.

The day of our departure was the most difficult in my life. I had come to feel half-Russian, I thought and counted in Russian, I recited Russian poetry and sang the Russian national anthem. I loved Svetya and Masha as sisters. And I would never feel as much love for anyone as I did for Petrovna. Except Mother, of course. I hardly remembered our life in Bialystok. I would not have actually minded to stay in Biysk.

Then my mind flipped. No, I don't want to stay in Biysk. Our old life came back to me in flashes of recognition, memories from the first half of my life. Since coming here, my life had been ugly. The coal train was disgusting, Old Mud had almost starved us; Biysk had no streets, no electricity, no running water, only the NKVD.

And a beloved library. When I came to say good-bye, Aksinia and Raisa, the greatest librarians in the world, handed me a satchel filled with books, and another with cookies and an apple cake.

"For the road," they said.

Aksina added through tears, "Remember Ralichka, whatever city you are in, the library will always be a welcoming place."

The snow was melting, as we boarded the train that would carry us back to Bialystok. Svetya wept, and so did I. Will I ever see the Vorontsevs again? I wondered.

Five years earlier, the train had sped like an uncaged tiger to evade the battlefield, but even then it took us two weeks to get here. Now, we were boarding a clean train with portable latrines and a supply of water, milk and bread. Our escorts carried pistols in their waists, not rifles, and were dressed in civilian clothes. But we knew that they were NKVD.

It was early morning at the Biysk Railroad Station, which was not a real station, but a flattened area where the conductors knew they had to stop. There was too much pain, and I was eager to get away. Abruptly, the wheels chugged and whirred. As we pulled out of the station, I saw Svetya and Masha running after the train, waving.

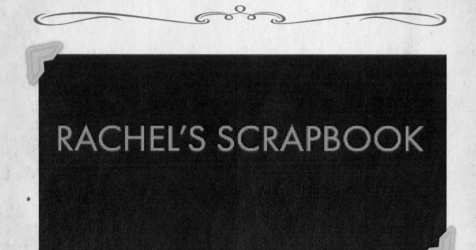

RACHEL'S SCRAPBOOK

The Rubinows in Bialystok, 1938. Esther, Jacob, Miss Julie -- Rala's governess, and Rala.

The Rubinow family in 1936. Esther, 10-year-old Wowka, Jacob and baby Rala.

Grandfather Rubinow.

Grandmother Jadwiga Rubinow -- famous dress designer.

Elena Frenkel Rakowski and
Rabbi Jacob Meyer Rakowski.

Baby Rala.
Rala, 2 years old.

The young revolutionary --
Puah Rakowski.

Jacob Rubinow --
age 23.

The orphanage marching in April, 1948 for the 5th anniverary of the Warsaw Ghetto destruction- Rala first row, left.

Rala -- upon her return to Bialystok in 1946.

Six of the girls-- Rala left.

Group picture of the Zionist Socialist Orphanage in Lodz-- Rala, second to left.

These are ALL the surviving Jewish children in Bialystok.
Rala-- last in front row to the
Right in white dress.

Picture on p. 105 of The Bialystok Memorial Book.

What the Gulag Old Mud looked like.

What the landscape in the city of Biysk looked like.

The Rubinows in Biysk, Siberia – 1945 Esther, Rala and Jacob.

Sunday in the park with mom-- Rala in Lodz with Mom.

Wowka Rubinow -- age 22 in Lodz.

Yakov Markovich Rubinow ---
Red Army soldier.

Vlodimir Yakovlevich Rubinow
-- Red Army soldier.

*The Primeval Forest between
Bialystok and Warsaw*- here,
the trains were stopped to
drag out and murder the
Jews.

PART THREE:
FROM POLAND WITH LOVE

CHAPTER TWENTY-NINE

As the train chugged west, the days became warmer.

"This is a much more pleasant journey than five years ago," Mother said.

Indeed, it was. I felt grown up, full of knowledge from all my books. What increased my good humor was the pretty dress Petrovna had sewn for me, which was my first-ever dress with a ruffle. My grandmother Jadwiga would have been proud of me.

The men escorting us were quite nice, dressed in normal men's clothes and speaking in normal voices. They had sucking candy and gave us kids a choice between strawberry or cherry flavors. The train moved slowly, so we could enjoy the countryside with its lush vegetation and black earth.

"The best soil to grow potatoes and vegetables," Father explained.

One day early in the afternoon, we stopped in a town called Dobra Matka, which is Ukrainian for The Good Mother. Our supervisors announced that we would remain here for two hours to replenish our food supplies and fuel. "So, it's a good time for young and old to go out and stretch your legs. You kids have room to jump hopscotch."

We were thrilled. I had already made some friends—two Davids, cousins whose parents lacked the imagination to give them individual names. Also, my new girlfriend Bracha, who had black braids and lustrous eyes.

We were inside the largest playground in the world. I don't mean playground exactly, but the enormous expanse of an abandoned railroad depot. Tracks ran in every direction, crisscrossing in so many places that if you stared at the ground, you'd end up hypnotized. The calm, in what in the past must have been the hub of whistling locomotives and chugging trains busily heading to useful destinations, was now breathtakingly weird.

With nothing here it was a challenge to play hide and seek. But that's exactly what we decided to do. I was chosen to seek. As the others dispersed, I covered my face with both hands, leaning against a wooden shack. My friends scrambled away so fast that soon their footsteps could no longer be heard.

I stood there, honor-bound not to look, waiting to give them enough time to hide. A vague sweet smell tickled my nostrils. As I pulled my hands away, the smell intensified, engaging my senses. Perfume in a shack on the railroad tracks in the Ukraine? Nothing in Biysk smelled like this. I remembered Mother's pretty perfume bottles back in Bialystok.

Oh, to hell with hide and seek, I must discover what's in the shack. I pushed a board, and it gave way easily. No door, so I crawled inside. Here the smell was overpowering, an intense aroma. Still, the darkness prevented me from locating the source.

Resolved, I crawled ahead. Soon I saw a little light coming from a hole in the ceiling, illuminating part of the shack

Before me were row upon row of lovely soap bars, all white, stretching as high as the ceiling. Gingerly I reached for a bar and turned it in my palms. Smooth and delicate to the touch, so unlike the slimy goo that passed for soap in Biysk. There was writing on it, in Polish letters, not Russian.

At that moment my friend Bracha returned, angry that I had neglected to look for them.

I interrupted with a shout of "Padam!" and revealed the soap.

"Oh," said Bracha, cuddling the soap. "There's a well not far away, so we can go there, get some water and wash up with this lovely soap."

I looked around. "No Davids." We giggled.

We brought up a bucket of water and undressed, staring at each other's nakedness.   "Are we beautiful?" Bracha asked.

"I don't know. So let's pretend that we are."

We poured water on ourselves and washed up, each with her own bar. Mmmm, our bodies were covered with delicious foam. We jumped and shivered. Then we washed away the foam and put our wet bodies into dry clothing. Not important—there were towels on the train. Our timing was perfect, ready to obey the train's first whistle.

We crawled back into the shack to load up on soap and bring as many bars as we could to our families. That done, we ran toward the train, carrying the soap in our aprons. Nearby were the Davids also headed for the train.

"We'll give them each a bar," I said, feeling magnanimous.

Bouncing onto the train, I shouted, "Mama, Papa! Look what we found."

Proudly Bracha and I displayed the soap.

The adults joined us and inspected the soap, wondering at its mysterious appearance.

"Look, Papa," I said. "There's writing on it in Polish. The letters R, J, F."

At that, Father and several other men who had served in the Red Army grabbed the bars of soap and started tossing them out of the train. What was going on? Bracha and I hugged each other in fear.

"Have we done something wrong?" I screamed.

This brought Father back to his senses. "Don't worry about it. It doesn't matter. Forget about it."

The Russian attendant grabbed a bar and inspected it. "Ah, you found the damned soap. I'm so sorry. We knew it existed, but didn't know where."

He threw it out of the train, saying, "RJF is German for Pure Jewish Fat."

Mother's face turned ashen. Her eyes exhibited such horror that I was afraid they might explode. Some adults cried.

Bracha's father said, "We heard rumors in the army that the Germans made soap out of Jewish flesh, but we didn't believe it."

Bracha and I were hysterical. We cried and tore at our clothes. We quickly undressed, not caring that we were naked in front of everyone. The attendant brought a pail of cold water, and we rinsed off.

I knew that this day would haunt me for the rest of my life.

CHAPTER THIRTY

It was mid-afternoon at the Bialystok Railroad Station. The sun shone brightly on filthy, unused tracks and platforms. We poured out of our car, and the Christians out of theirs. As Father had remarked when we boarded the train, "Going into captivity, Stankiewicz and Dolinska had no choice but to ride with Jews. Now it's different."

The Poles were fresh and energized, happily spilling out of the train, their bodies energized, anticipation in their eyes. They rushed ahead without as much as a glance at us. My father's gaze pierced them with hate. The sounds of their joy and laughter were heard by those of us who stood at a distance, observing.

I watched them hug and kiss loved ones they hadn't seen in five years. I had a few tears in my eyes, so my gaze was a little foggy, like watching a film at the community hall in Biysk. Count Stankiewicz was kissing a fat woman, who must have been the Countess he had left behind. Countess Dolinska was handed flowers and packages from what looked like a large family.

I stood close to my parents and was soon joined by Bracha and the Davids. They didn't look astonished by what was happening. At that moment we noticed Mr. Zygmund Kobielski, the saddle maker and my former Polish poetry teacher at our short-lived afternoon school.

"Call him," Bracha urged, "he likes you because you memorized the poem by Adam Mickiewicz."

His back was turned, so I called out, "Mr. Zygmund! Mr. Zygmund!"

Silence in the Polish group, as they turned around to look at me. Mr. Zygmund seemed delighted at the sound of my voice. He smiled broadly and advanced toward our group. "Ah, Rala, nice to see you!"

But he did not make it very far. Two men, who must have been from his family, caught up with him and whispered something that made him walk off with them.

The sun was still shining, but I felt chilled. From where we stood, Bialystok's ruins were visible on the horizon. I remembered what Dima had tried to tell me when he was mad, about returning here. And, of course, the bad Dima was always right. More tears came to my eyes as the ruins dimmed in the sinking sun.

When the boisterous Poles departed, Father told Bracha and the Davids to rejoin their parents. There were about a hundred of us on the platform, silent, but not shocked. We needed to think. Hard.

After a while, Father said, "We should have known that no arrangements would be made for our arrival. The Russians let us go, but the Poles don't want us."

People nodded, confused.

Bracha's father ventured, "Perhaps we should have written to the Bialystok Municipality..." He stopped and laughed at the incongruity.

So what now?

I had a terrible stomachache. It started on the train and increased with every day of our journey. As painful as it was, I knew I couldn't possibly complain right then.

We noticed a few men in coveralls on the platform, probably railroad workers. Father called out to them, asking if there was a telephone and a directory anywhere, but they ignored him. Resigned, we sat down on our luggage. The adults gave us kids water from bottles the NKVD had given us as parting gifts. Used to Siberian outhouses, people relieved themselves behind the railroad tracks in an orderly fashion.

Father and Reb Yossi huddled together, with everyone staring and praying that these two sages would come up with a solution. "We can stay here overnight and sleep on our suitcases," said Reb Yossi. "We have some food and water. After a night's sleep, we'll walk into town tomorrow."

Father objected. "It's too dangerous to be here overnight. We don't want a rumor to start that a bunch of Jews are occupying the station."

So it was agreed that we proceed into town. We picked up our bundles, ready to move. It was dark, with no city lights anywhere. We literally felt our way out of the railroad station.

At this moment of our indecision, we heard loud honking, followed by lights. Two trucks, similar to those we had seen in Siberia, advanced in our direction. A couple of men jumped out of the cabs, and several more from inside the trucks.

As they approached, they shouted in Yiddish, "Hello, hello, fellow Jews! We are the Bialystok Jewish Committee."

They came over, shaking hands with the adults and lifting the little kids—not me!—in the air. We kissed and hugged these strangers, the empty dark station reverberating with our applause.

People whispered in astonishment, "These boys have guns."

A young man dressed in a green Red Army tunic addressed us briefly. "From now on you have nothing to worry about. We have homes and food. And trust us, we'll protect you."

"If we are back home, why do we need protection," I asked Father, in a too-loud whisper.

The man in the tunic overheard me. "You will see, young lady, that we must protect ourselves."

The trucks moved along through darkness and hushed silence. Here and there the headlights illuminated piles of scorched black stones, as if a conflagration had taken place not long ago. The wheels kicked up ash and we coughed, which reminded us of the coal trains five years ago.

The trucks stopped in front of a huge building of massive red brick, with a padlocked gate. The drivers honked, summoning half a dozen people with torches, who opened the gate to let us in. Immediately the torchbearers bolted the gate and wrapped chains around the lock.

The torchlights revealed a steeple with a cross on it. Bizarre— it was a monastery! The structure looked old but well preserved, though with burn marks in many places. The flickering torches caused the steeple and cross to appear detached from the building and floating in air.

"My father wouldn't have believed that we ended up here," Mother said. The mention of Grandfather made her cry. Others in our midst laughed, perhaps for the same reason that Mother cried.

"All will be well," we heard a reassuring voice say. "Please, come in for supper."

The interior was as frigid as monasteries are reputed to be, the chambers constructed with heavy stones. Was it a Christian test to freeze its most pious members? We knew we would be fine eventually, not because of the Christian god, but because spring was coming.

With this encouraging thought, I followed my parents into the dining room, another stone chamber. In the center were two long wooden tables with benches on both sides.

"Oh, Jesus of Nazareth!" exclaimed Mr. Rosenberg, an acquaintance from the train ride.

This was a common Polish utterance used by Christians and sometimes by Jews to express surprise. But should Jews use it in a monastery?

Reb Yossi looked puzzled. "Let us agree that from now on the Christian references you might have used before are out."

My stomach pain intensified, and I asked Mother to find me a bathroom. I was shown a stone cubicle with a hole in the ground. It was worse than the Siberian outhouse.

I washed my hands and returned to the dining room. About a dozen young men and women waited for us. Their leader was obviously the young man from the railroad station, still dressed in his Red Army tunic. He had reddish-blond hair, delicate features and a muscled body. He looked young.

"My name is Max," he said, "but they call me Commander Igor, which is my partisan forest name." His comrades applauded and whistled. "All of these upstanding citizens," he motioned to his group, "were together in the forest in the Bialystok area. When this we were liberated, we joined the Red Army and continued to fight." He grinned sheepishly. "Now. let's eat."

Mother whispered, "Rala, why did you spend so much time in the bathroom?"

"Because I have stomach cramps."

"Oh, my God. We cannot have you sick."

We were served a tasty pea soup with black bread and slices of cheese. The adults drank hot tea with lumps of sugar. The kids drank milk.

"These boys and girls are not much older than Wowka," Mother remarked. The astonishment at their youth was shared by everyone. As our hosts, they walked around, from time to time reassuring us with, "Everything will be all right. Nothing to worry about."

The next day, we slept very late. We washed and ate breakfast of cream of wheat and hard-boiled eggs, with milk for the children and tea for the adults. Mother and Father were holding hands. Maybe living in a religious institution, even a monastery, made them show affection for each other.

Commander Igor, wearing a Russian peasant shirt, greeted us with a benevolent smile. "Good afternoon." Everyone laughed in a carefree manner, perhaps because we were protected by young Jewish fighters. "Let me introduce my comrades, Tsipi Zukerman, David Chodorovsky, David Landau, so many Davids..." The names went on, maybe twenty in all.

"How did you end up in this monastery?" someone asked.

Commander Igor spread his arms. "Excellent question. We came here last September and discovered that there were a few unused monasteries and convents. We liked this one best, St. Stefan's, named after our own Polish saint." Again, uninhibited laughter. "Also, it is located on a hill, has a strong gate, and is far from the city. We have named it 'The Fortress.'"

So, this was our new reality—a city of ruins, and a few Jews occupying a defensive position on high grounds.

More from Igor: "We are the only Jewish Committee in Bialystok County, but we are in touch with committees in Warsaw and Lodz, which are in direct contact with Zionist organizations in Palestine and America. We want everyone to know that we are not alone. Jews around the world support us." Applause.

Our living quarters were unusual. Apparently, monks had slept on narrow cots for centuries because they had dedicated themselves to a life of suffering. But why? God had something to do with it, but I didn't understand why he should bother with stupid people who prefer to sleep on cots instead of normal beds. Over each cot was a nail on which, Father explained, a crucifix must have hung, but which had been removed by Commander Igor and his pals.

With so many cells, we Rubinows appropriated two. As I sat on the cot in my cell, I wondered what had happened to the monks. Nothing good, of that I was sure. They must have vanished as Father Jerzy Kwiat had. The good part was that now I had my own room. I was ten years old, and never before had I enjoyed a moment's privacy.

I walked over to my parents' cell and heard Mother's voice. "I have been looking at this boy who calls himself Commander Igor. He resembles Fanya's son, Bronek. The blond hair and blue eyes. All these years I have been confident that Bronek is alive. He was always mistaken for an Aryan."

Father observed her with pity. "Most Jewish boys with blond hair and blue eyes are dead. And he is older than Bronek would have been."

I left them and retreated to my cell. More like a dungeon than a place to sleep. This made me think of Alexander Dumas' Man in the Iron Mask. I lay down on my cot, which by now had acquired a pillow and two blankets. I reached for one of the books Raisa and Aksinya, my favorite Biysk librarians, had gifted me. It was poetry by Samuil Marshak that rhymed well and was often funny. My favorite was one about Mister Twister from America, who was on a trip around the world with his wife, daughter, and their pet monkey.

Mister Twister

A former minister

Mister Twister millionaire

Owner of factories

Shipyards and mills

Visits the world

With its cities and hills.

The gist of this long poem was that no country would admit this arrogant rich American who had made his fortune on the back of black slaves. So, Mr. Twister, wife, monkey and daughter, go back to America. But, in a "twist," America doesn't want them either!

The moral: No one loves a monkey!

One morning, Commander Igor and another partisan called Srulik, left early in the truck and returned with a strange-looking contraption. Something enormous and metallic. It slid off the truck onto a platform with wheels and was moved with difficulty to its permanent position on the monastery's roof, next to the cross that was visible for kilometers.

It was an amazing piece of something. Father, as usual, resolved the mystery. "It's a cannon. Very old."

"Very good. Mr. Rubinow," said Srulik. "It's from the days of Napoleon Bonaparte. Probably left in Countess Walewska's bedroom." The Countess, Mother later explained, was Napoleon's Polish sweetheart. Did our own Countess Dolinska have a cannon in her bedroom?

"And what can it do?" someone asked.

Commander Igor laughed as if this were the best joke in years. "Absolutely nothing! Zero! But it makes a huge noise. Also, sitting on the roof it looks menacing. And to scare them further, if necessary, we'll bang this thing with hammers and shovels."

"Papa," I asked, "who are 'them?'"

He thought for a minute, but all he said was, "It's not important, Ralichka. You don't need to know. Not yet."

The Fortress was run like a commune, with everyone performing a valuable service because this commune was poor. With having the support of the whole Jewish world and America, why did we still use the monks' spoons and forks? Everything in this Fortress felt temporary, as people, and even furniture, were thrown together pell-mell. The worst example was our inability to send or receive letters at a time when we desperately needed to communicate. Why? Because the monastery was not listed on a postal route, seeing as the idea of being a monk was to distance yourself from your family and friends. And the Almighty does not need a postal address.

The solution was to write without expecting an answer, not in the near future, anyway. So we wrote to Zila, Mina and Sonya in Palestine. To the Vorontsevs in Biysk, and to Uncle Marek in a gulag of which we had only a post office box. What would they do to him now that they no longer needed his expertise in German, Japanese and Italian?

"Don't worry," Father said. "Marek is an expert in survival."

Mother told me that without Father's knowledge, she had written a letter to Wowka at his military post office box in Germany.

CHAPTER THIRTY-ONE

The monastery sat on a hill overlooking the ruins of Bialystok's Jewish Quarter, where, at the time we left, Grandfather Jacob Meyer had lived with Aunt Fanya, her husband Grisha and my cousin Bronek. Looking down from atop the monastery we could see directly into the ruins. From everywhere we turned on our hill, all we could see were these ruins. Not a single house remained standing. You got hypnotized staring at something that never moves.

Over the weeks, I observed people descending downhill from the Fortress into the ruins. A person or two at a time. Mother held back, and I said nothing, in hope of avoiding this painful pilgrimage. But I knew that one day it would happen.

That day arrived. "Rala, we'll go down to find your grandfather's house."

Mother and I walked down from the top of the hill into the ashes below. We were alone, so we could dig in privacy. I was crippled with fear. What if we found a skeleton in the ruins? I suggested to Mother that perhaps we should go back up and ask

Father to come down and help us dig. She stared at me as if I were insane.

The shape of the ruins revealed that the homes here were small. What remained of them were piles of charred wood and brick, as if the houses had fallen down on themselves, collapsing and turning into pitiful debris. I remembered from visiting Grandfather that Kupiecka Street where he lived was paved. No pavement remained anywhere. Roads and sidewalks had been obliterated alongside the houses they anchored. Street names were gone. Letters, originally carved into wooden poles, had been destroyed by explosions and fires.

"Rala, do you remember Grandfather's address?"

"Number 14 Kupiecka Street."

Her eyes shone with pride. I knew she was testing me, because this was an address she would never forget. It was warm but windy, the ash swirling in the air and making it hard to breathe. Mother paced between the heaps, muttering to herself. After some reflection, she stopped before a pile indistinguishable from any other and declared, "This is my house."

She might have been right because every house looked the same. She knelt in the rubble, digging into it with both hands. Working in a frenzy, she tossed away charred boards and bricks. I also dug and pulled out a few burned rags, a cracked plate and part of a blanket that fell apart in my hands. Most importantly, we retrieved pages with Hebrew letters on them. Pages and more pages were buried in these ruins. Mother grabbed a handful, scrutinizing them closely.

"I know these are pages from my father's Bible. Burned, dead scrolls." She placed the scraps in between two handkerchiefs she had brought with her. Then she rose, shaking the dust off her hands. "I can't stay here even for another minute."

We turned around and climbed back to the monastery. This would be our only visit to hell. That night I had terrible stomach pain.

There were about two dozen children in the monastery, and we ranged in age between four and thirteen. And we needed schooling, but how? Someone named us "The New Bialystok Jewish School" Next? As in Russia, use local talent.

Commander Igor and his friends, none of whom had children, started our education by ordering us to stay in the dining room after breakfast for classes. A partisan called Frieda brought in a blackboard and chalk. We were delighted to be handed our own notebooks and pencils. Everything looked perfect. So, may the learning begin!

Commander Igor was persuaded to be our first teacher. "Today we'll learn about the place of Jews in the history of the world. It's a huge place…"

The little ones fell asleep immediately. I did not sleep, daydreaming instead of the princes hiding in a monster's castle who was not really a monster but a beautiful prince who… Poor Commander Igor continued, pretending to be unaware of our lack of attention. "In September 1939, the Third Reich attacked Poland…"

Now everyone was asleep.

The next day, another fighter, Haim, went on and on describing his life in the forest, where he survived by eating berries and mice. Everyone yelled "Disgusting!" and pretended to gag.

Matters worsened when other fighters chose to tell us gruesome tales about how Jews—"perhaps you own relatives"—were beaten and tortured. Terrible stories filled with broken bones and blood. Little kids cried, big kids cried, everyone had nightmares, and Commander Igor suspended school.

More ingenuity was needed. Igor approached Father. "Mr. Rubinow, I have just learned that you used to be a high school mathematics teacher. So it might be a great idea to teach the children mathematics, and take their minds off war stories."

Father courageously accepted the challenge. Luckily, he was more successful with us than he had been with youngsters in his youth. He taught on a high level, and I didn't understand much. But the girls liked his voice, though I knew it was unremarkable. They said he was "cute," and that was very true. Which begged the question: Being married to my "cute" Father, why did Mother need a Count?

Father decided to submit us to an oral test that he called "revision." Naturally, the exercise proved again that only a few understood his lofty mathematical concepts. Less frustrated than in his youth, he repeated his favorite axiom: "Math is the simplest discipline in science."

We kept writing letters to people we loved, not expecting replies. It was a satisfactory, though one-sided, correspondence. And then, a breakthrough! Somehow Commander Igor had persuaded someone in the Municipality to grant our monastery an official address. Now, we were receiving letters from my aunts in Palestine, which contained a wavering, timid question. "How is Bialystok?" Nothing yet from Marek or Wowka.

Commander Igor warned, "Please do not write to anyone in the Soviet Union, because the NKVD may arrest them for corresponding abroad."

One letter arrived, not exactly from Russia, but from the Red Army stationed in Germany. "Dear Mama," Wowka wrote. "I was saddened by your letter about the heartache you felt when confronted with what had happened to our family. You should have followed my example and renounced the stinking piece of paper that is your Polish citizenship. I have a wonderful life in Germany. Whatever we need, we confiscate from these Fascists. And the German frauleins love Red Army soldiers. I love you. Your son forever, Wowka."

CHAPTER THIRTY-TWO

Jews were not the only ones living in the monastery. There was a Christian man, a young priest who lived in a separate apartment down the hill. You could not reach him from inside, only from the courtyard and down a stone path that led to the Jewish ruins.

One morning I decided to pay him a visit. For the most part it was curiosity about why he had remained here all alone. Another was my hope of obtaining books to read, because I was not allowed, as were no children, to go to the public library, for fear of being attacked. The adults had also been cautioned by Commander Igor to go out as little as possible. Since Grandfather Jacob Meyer's house was full of books, I reasoned, so would be this priest's. Maybe he had nice books to make me escape the endless stories the partisans told about Jews dying in terrible ways. Or worse, taking math lessons from my father.

The priest's apartment was seven steps down from the courtyard. The door was heavy, with rusted hinges, like haunted houses in the frightening ghost stories I loved to read. His door was unlocked, because the rusty hinges were down. I checked myself to make sure that my braids were neatly tied with the red ribbons from Biysk, and that the dress that Petrovna had made for me was recently laundered.

I grabbed the door handle and almost fell back from pulling so hard. So I knocked. Nothing, not even an echo. If he was in some cavern inside, he could not possibly have heard my feeble knock. I climbed onto a rock and peered into a window. Pressing my face to the misty glass, I saw a tall man in a black cassock.

I knocked on the glass, shouting: "Hello sir, priest! Please open the door. I am from the monastery, and I came to ask you if you have a book I can read."

Magic! This man was just like Aksinya and Raisa. He heard a child saying the word "book," and the heavy doors flew open. Well, they didn't actually fly, but gritted aside. Inside, I curtsied. He was thin, as thin as Dima when he had returned from the war. He introduced himself as Father Paul, and I said that I was Rala Rubinow.

"Sir, I would like to borrow a book. Please."

He smiled. He beamed. The tall thin man grew taller and fatter. And just as in Biysk, he asked, "Would you like some milk and cake?"

I was not as hungry as I had been in Biysk, but not stupid enough to refuse an offer of milk and cake. I nodded and followed him inside.

"This is the rectory," he explained.

It looked like a small version of our dining hall, except that the walls were lined with bookshelves. Father Paul sneezed and wiped his nose, as I had seen many of our people do because of the cold and dampness of these ancient stones. He was older than

I had thought, but not as old as my father.

There was a crucifix on the wall and a large silver cross hanging from Father Paul's neck, so I was honor-bound to be frank with him before eating his cake. "Thank you very much for your kindness, but I must warn you that I cannot become a Christian because my grandfather was a great rabbi here in Bialystok."

He laughed hard, wiping tears from his eyes.

"Conversion is not expected, I promise."

The cake was hard and studded with raisins. I remembered the raisin challah at my brother's Bar Mitzvah seven years earlier, when I had sat next to Grandfather, picking out the raisins and stacking them in a pile. Now I ate the raisins and found them delicious. That is how things change.

"I see you love raisins?"

"The last time I saw them was at my brother's Bar Mitzvah, which was at my Grandfather's synagogue right down this hill…" I felt my eyes filling with tears, because I remembered how Mother and I had descended below.

He looked at me differently, somehow. "I am so sorry, child. So terribly sorry."

I looked up at him and smiled. "Do you want to see the best way to eat crumbs?" I put the cake in between my palms and turned them into crumbs. Then I wet my fingers with saliva, as in Biysk, and put them in my mouth. "Yum. Want to try?"

Father Paul did the same, and I could see that he appreciated it.

"So," I asked at last, "how about my book?"

He took me to the nearest bookshelf. "Do you like books about saints?"

"I don't really know who they are, because in Russia it's against the law to like saints. The only priest I met before you, was Father Jerzy Kwiat. But I think the Russians killed him. So which saint do you recommend?"

"For you, I would start with a girl saint. I am certain you will enjoy reading about Saint Theresa of Avila. She was a lovely Spanish girl."

I thanked my new friend, Father Paul, and clawed my way back to the compound, clutching my book. Once in my room, I started reading. The paper was smooth to the touch, full of colorful illustrations showing important ladies and gentlemen dressed in crimson and purple, velvet and brocade. This girl, Theresa, was a rich noblewoman who was compassionate and distributed food to the poor. Because of her devotion to Jesus, she built monasteries and convents. Page after page, she traveled around Spain, distributing food and praying. A great deal of praying. So far, terribly boring.

But in a book, as I knew from my extensive reading, something must happen to disturb the peace, preferably something exciting. What happened to Theresa, was that she died. After her death, all the cities in Spain fought for her body to be buried in their cemeteries, imagining that the presence of her holy bones would make cripples walk and consumption sufferers stop coughing. That's it. Stupid!

"Your Theresa is completely boring," I reported to Father Paul.

He handed me another book. "You will find this exciting."

The next day in class a partisan called Antek told us about naked people in the shower… But he couldn't get any further, because Commander Igor jumped up and dragged him away by his collar, saying something rapidly that sounded to me like the worst Russian curses.

Time to read the new book from Father Paul. The hero was Saint Sebastian, a brave Roman general. This time the lush drawings portrayed Roman soldiers whose uniforms consisted not of pants, but charming metal skirts worn with lace-up sandals. The not-charming part came when the Romans discovered that secretly Sebastian was the Christian for whom they had been hunting for a long time.

Poor Sebastian! Legionnaires ripped off his clothes, though in the picture they left a piece of cloth to cover his bottom, and hung him stretched between two trees. Then they amused themselves by riding around and shooting arrows into him. In each drawing there was more and more red blood. The bloody holes in his body left by arrows were hideous. Another page, more of the same. I couldn't believe Sebastian still had so much blood.

I shall kill Father Paul! I had power over him because I was his only parishioner. He must have suspected trouble, because milk and cake were already laid out. Chocolate cake! I had never eaten chocolate cake. To hell with Sebastian. I sat down and savored the cake, taking dainty sips of milk between bites.

"That is so good." I wiped my hands and face. "Father Paul, this story about Sebastian is disgusting. I think adults are crazy. The fighters and the partisans tell us stories about naked people in showers and children in striped pajamas. Terrible, awful stories. And now you give these monstrous books." I raised my arms, as if pleading with God.

"Oh, I never thought about it this way," he said. "Forgive me. Because I live alone, I am becoming an idiot. Very well, now tell me what books do you really want to read."

"I want to read 'The Count of Monte Cristo." Also books about cowboys and Indians in America."

"I think the library has them under 'Books of General Interest.' Early tomorrow morning, I'll head there and bring you pleasant adventures."

CHAPTER THIRTY-THREE

April sunshine and the promise of a blooming spring caused anxiety among us Fortress residents. The temporary nature of our lives was brought into sharper focus. There was a sensation that winds of change were blowing our way.

Some of the unrest was due to the remnants of Jewish property. Somehow, after many inquiries and demands, Commander Igor persuaded the Bialystok Municipality to allow people from the Fortress to look at the lists of Jewish property still standing.

This caused jubilation, which was hard to understand, because most of the Jewish property in the city lay in ruins outside our windows ,and most of the people here had not been property owners before the war. Still, it was a victory.

Father knew exactly what it meant. "Jewish property in the Aryan neighborhood. Too bad we did not own our building."

Nevertheless, my parents resolved to head for the municipality archives to search the books. The next day they ate an early breakfast and marched into town.

When they returned, Father was rubbing his hands with contentment, but Mother was more reserved. I overheard them speaking in their cell. "I don't feel very comfortable with what I did," she said.

"Fira, everyone does it. It's a crime not to do it! The house is your brother's and his wife's property, and sadly, neither Tanya nor Lova are coming back. At least when we sell it, we'll have enough money to get out of here and start over."

"Yes, Kuba, I understand. But you made me take an oath that I am Tanya Rakowski, and I signed a false statement. It bothers me."

"Forget it. Think about what we can do for Rala when we have the money."

Father was right; everyone did it. People claimed properties of cousins and uncles, or even those belonging to people they had never met or heard of. Why not? Now my parents and many others waited for a notification from the municipality that their claim had been processed and the building was theirs to sell. The only property I was interested in was the apartment where we used to live. I resolved that somehow I would get out of where we were and make my way to the building on Zwirki Wigura Avenue.

I needed a strategy. My first thought was to ask Father Paul for advice. On second thought, it was a bad idea, because he would offer to take me to town, which my parents and Commander Igor would not allow.

Third thought, I had none.

I had to see Father Paul, but I wouldn't tell him about my strategy.

"Please, find more books for me," I begged. "I don't know any more titles."

He nodded. "I will ask the librarian for help. I'll tell them it's for a ten-year old who reads like a fourteen-year old."

"Thank you very much. May I have some cake?"

"Oh, of course. Today it's orange with vanilla frosting."

He brought me the cake, and, of course, milk. He also poured some milk for himself and cut another piece of cake.

"We are like two people having a treat in a restaurant." I remarked.

"You are going to be an excellent flirt, Rala."

I laughed. "That's exactly what Dima said."

He wanted to know about Dima, and I told him the whole story. After I finished, he was pensive.

"Rala, I think it's time you learned the Lord's Prayer."

"Oh, no!" I stamped my foot. "I already told that I am not becoming a Christian."

This time he was serious.

"Knowing the Lord's Prayer is for your protection. Hear me out. If you are attacked here in Bialystok or anywhere else in Poland, you must stand before the hoodlums and scream the Lord's Prayer. I don't mean mumble, I mean scream to high heaven, and I guarantee they will let you go."

"This is very good frosting, Father Paul. But, are you sure it's all right to misuse God's name? You see, my mother says that I should respect Christianity and should never say 'Jesus of Nazareth.'"

"Yes, you shouldn't do it frivolously, but one day, it may be an emergency."

So we began. "'Our Father, who art in heaven, hallowed be thy name. Thy kingdom come.' You must say it naturally, as if you have been doing it all your life. 'Thy will be done in earth as it is in heaven.'"

The practice continued for a little longer, until I memorized it, but it still did not come naturally to me.

"Do you pay for my cake or the Christian Church?" I asked him.

"It's the Church. I swore a vow of poverty." Back to my strategy of visiting my home and doing it as soon as possible. If Father were to sell Uncle Lova's house, we would leave Bialystok for a safer place. My project was to observe which car was traveling into town and when. We had the two trucks that had picked us up at the railroad station and a car that might have been as old as Napoleon's cannon.

The result of my observations: One truck traveled every other day to the marketplace to buy fruits and vegetables. That's the one! It would go out about 9:00 a.m. and be back by noon. The next day, Antek and Dashek, another Aryan-looking boy, would be driving to the marketplace. I left the dining room before them and hid in the back, among burlap sacks. I forced myself to stop breathing. When we reached the market called Rynek Kosciuszki, I slid out and disappeared.

I ran for a bit and came upon two old men in a doorway smoking pipes. With a perfect curtsy I asked for directions to Zwirki Wigura Avenue.

"It's across the street from the city park and the Branicki Palace," one of them told me.

After five years of absence, I stepped into the avenue with trees. I crossed the park, walked along the Bialka River and stood before the gate leading to the Branicki Palace. But where was the Ritz Hotel? Where it had once stood was a spectacular ruin, like a smashed-up cathedral. The Germans were crazy to blow up such a nice hotel, I thought.

Then I reached our building, number sixteen. My heart was pounding like a drum. The courtyard looked the same. The gray cobblestone walk, the windows with potted plants behind chintz curtains, towels and sheets drying on balconies. I pressed my body into the wall for fear of being discovered.

"Our Father, who art in heaven…." I mumbled the Lord's Prayer, so I wouldn't forget. Up one flight, looking as it was before, now dirtier, up another, then to the right, toward apartment seven. The number was still on the door, with someone else's name. Very slowly, I eased the door open and slid in. If they saw me, kaput to my life.

I was now in our long corridor leading to the salon. The place was frightfully dark, which it had never been in the past. The apartment reeked of cabbage. Mother had never allowed cabbage to be cooked in our home. Fine peoples' apartments do not smell of cabbage, she said. I felt as if I were walking deeper and deeper through a dark tunnel..

Suddenly, there was a shaft of light, which I followed into the salon, forgetting all caution. What I needed to see was my painting of the three cows drinking water from an endless brook that Uncle Marek's friend had given us.

Light shimmered through my mother's drapes, illuminating the piano. I wondered if anyone there could play it. The Persian rug was gone, and the wooden floor, Mother's and Marysia's pride, was stubby and coarse. The entire apartment felt dirty and unkempt. But from where I stood, I saw the fireplace. There were two men and a woman seated at a table I didn't recognize, eating something that smelled like kielbasa. They had not yet noticed me.

No use hiding anymore, so I walked into the salon. And there they were: My three cows, drinking water from the still endless brook.

"Who the hell are you, kid? " The threesome stopped chewing and stared at me, too shocked to speak. I was scared of them and they were terrified of me, believing apparently that I was a ghost.

"Jews are seen all over town!" shouted the woman. "They're not gone for good. They're back."

Should I yell the Lord's Prayer now, or wait until they hit me?

"This is my apartment and my parents and my brother's!" I cried out. "And the cows over the fireplace are also mine!"

And that's when I turned around and ran as fast as I could. Out of the door and down the steps. I heard footsteps following me. As soon as I was down, I hid behind the stairs, thinking that they would have chased me into the street. But they didn't bother. Maybe they were too eager to return to their kielbasa.

I came out from under the staircase and, affecting a nonchalant gait, walked out of the courtyard and toward the marketplace, where I hoped to find our truck. I spotted Antek and Dashek haggling with a farmer over a bag of cucumbers. My brain was too tired to make up stories, so I approached them with the truth, expecting a scolding. Instead, they applauded my "spirit" and anointed me an "honorary partisan." I rode back squeezed between tomatoes and cucumbers.

The Fortress was in a panic, with everyone looking for me. Mother paced around the courtyard, wringing her hands.

Father tried to calm her, but she yelled at him, "You evil-hearted bastard! You don't care about your children!"

When we drove into the compound, I climbed out of the truck carrying a bag of tomatoes. Mother threw the tomatoes on the ground and slapped me hard with the back of her hand. People were too shocked to speak, because even among us nervous souls, no one slapped their little girls.

Father stepped up and carried me away.

"I was in our apartment," I whispered.

CHAPTER THIRTY-FOUR

The end of April ushered in fantastic weather, warmly caressing our bodies.

"Enjoy it for a while longer," Father reminded us. "This is but a stop on our road to Palestine."

From day to day, people in the monastery grew more impatient, angry that the lovely weather, which should have represented freedom, accentuated our trap in a prison surrounded by wild beasts.

At the height of our frustration, we received a message that the beasts were about to strike. It was conveyed to Commander Igor by Father Paul. Apparently, a priest in the largest church in Bialystok had told his parishioners that on Passover, Jews on the hill—meaning us— might have kidnapped a Christian child to use his blood for baking matzoh. Father Paul advised us to leave soon and carefully, over time and in small groups.

There was but one way out: the train to Warsaw.

It was a dangerous trip, worse than living in the Fortress. This train crossed the most ancient forests in Europe, dense, impenetrable and primeval. The death threat for Jews were the Polish forces of the National Army connected to the Polish Government in London, the one that had liberated us from Old Mud (funny!) but had been outlawed by the new Communist government. The National Army retreated into the forests to fight the Communists. But while they trained to do so, they found an easier target: Jews riding the train from Bialystok to Warsaw.

The first to leave were the Grossmans, husband and wife, their daughter, my good friend Bracha, and Mrs. Grossman's mother, Fruma Shustak. We hugged and kissed, promising each other to meet in Palestine.

A few days later the Resnick brothers, Aaron and Shimon, announced their intention to leave. Aaron, twenty-eight, and Shimon, thirty-one, called themselves "unconfirmed bachelors," who intended to sail to Palestine and marry the first two girls who would have them.

Every morning Commander Igor inspected the premises at five a.m. The morning after the brothers' departure, he discovered Aaron's and Shimon's bloodied bodies outside our gate. The partisans removed the bodies and washed the blood off the cobblestones. Later in the day, we children learned that the Resnicks had died, but not the details.

The next morning after breakfast, Commander Igor called a general meeting.

"We are here because last night Aaron and Shimon Resnick were murdered by the National Army. Here is how they operate: They stop almost every train in the densest part of the forest, board it, and walk from car to car looking for Jews. You may be a Christian, but if you look Jewish, they grab you and pull you off the train. It's very unpredictable."

"But why?" someone shouted, which brought on laughter. Even I, at age ten, knew that Poles didn't need a reason to kill a Jew.

"I think I just learned something about us Jews," said Igor. "We survived this last terrible disaster because we learned to laugh at death straight in the face. Incredible! But seriously, last night my comrades and I decided that from now on, one of us will accompany every family on the train. This is not a request, but an order. So remember, no one travels alone."

For the next two weeks, most people obeyed Commander Igor's orders not to board a train without armed escort. Whatever happened, the travelers lived, and the escorts returned safely.

July came with sweltering heat that made Mother begin to reminisce.

"Before the war this was vacation season, when Wowka and I would go into the mountains…."

The rage in Father's eyes made her stop mid-sentence. I couldn't stand it any longer and left their cell.

One morning, Father Paul came over and asked to speak to Commander Igor. It must have been something very secretive, because Igor went down to the rectory to talk with him.

His face was ashen when he returned. Silently, he and Antek got into the truck and stormed out of the gate. The others locked us in with extra caution. Sometime later, the two returned in a cloud of dust. I had never seen either of them so angry.

"Only the adults," said Igor. "Is this understood? No one under sixteen is allowed into the dining room."

The adults emerged from the meeting as silent as ghosts. Only one word was whispered: "Kielce."

I walked over to my parents and grabbed Father's hand. Mother's eyes stared motionlessly into the void, and I wasn't sure if she was aware of her surroundings. Then she looked at me and started hugging me so fiercely I thought she might crack my ribs.

There was only one person who would tell me the truth, because he considered me an almost-adult. Father Paul. I went down to his rectory.

He said, "Igor is one of the bravest men I have ever seen. And the most honest. So if he doesn't think children should hear about this…."

"No! If you don't tell me the truth, someone else will, and they may lie and exaggerate and it'll be scarier."

"Yes, very convincing. Yesterday in the city of Kielce, which is far away from here, a mob of drunk Polish hooligans attacked the Jews who had returned to live in town. They lived together in a house belonging to the Jewish Committee. The Poles killed forty-three Jews."

I sat down and began to cry.

"There are maybe a hundred of us in here."

He brought me a glass of water.

"Commander Igor and I are afraid that Poles in Bialystok may try to do the same to you. But maybe not, because this monastery is like a fortress, which is what you call it."

My stomach began to hurt terribly, so I excused myself and went back up to my parents. When I told Mother about my stomach, she became upset.

"Oh, no, please don't be sick. I can't take it."

I went to my cell and lay down. When we get out of here, I told myself, I'll ask Father to find me some medicine. In the meantime, I forced myself to lay still and felt better. But at night I developed diarrhea and went several times to the lavatory. At breakfast, I told one of the servers, Magda, that my stomach hurt. She brought me oatmeal and a cup of tea. I felt better, until I heard a whisper behind me.

"Besides the dead there were a dozen wounded who were taken to the hospital where they were attacked by Polish patients."

I could not finish my oatmeal.

Some good news did occur, however. Two days after Kielce, six new fighters came to our fortress from Baranowicze, a nearby town. Serious plans were afoot to evacuate Bialystok in a safe and orderly fashion.

My parents asked Antek and Dashek to give them a ride into town when they went on their daily shopping route. I was asleep when they returned, awakened by their improbable screams.

"You, you—" Mother was choking. "I always knew I didn't marry Albert Einstein, but I never thought I married such a cretin!"

I heard a slap, loud and clear. "And you didn't marry into Polish nobility!"

Oh, my God, everything that was wrong with my parents before had turned awful since we returned. I ran into their cell to try and stop the fight.

Mother turned to me and said, "Your genius father thought I could impersonate Tanya Rakowski, my brother Lova's wife, and claim their property. But what he forgot was that Tanya had the weirdest bulging eyes in town, and that someone was bound to remember. And guess what? Someone did, and now the police are after us!"

"This is nonsense," Father said, defending himself. "Every Jew claims whatever property remains. Anyway, stop the shouting, because we must catch the very next train to Warsaw."

I was tired, more tired than ever before.

"But we can't travel alone!" I said. "And Commander Igor needs time to prepare an escort."

Father was adamant.

"No time for this. You don't want to see your parents in prison."

I ran down the hill to say good-bye to Father Paul. He hugged me and gave me all the cake he had in his house. Upstairs, I packed my precious possessions: my stamp collection consisting of letters from Zila, Mina and Sonya in Palestine. It had grown, because my aunts were eager correspondents.

Igor was worried to see us travel by ourselves, but Father explained what had happened, excluding the part about the bulging eyes. He drove us to the railroad station and bought the tickets. We parted without kissing or hugging, not because we didn't love him, but because we were emotionally drained.

At the railroad station, we concocted a hasty plan. Father said that we must travel in separate cars. Mother was blonde and blue-eyed and spoke perfect Polish, so she could easily pass for a Christian. To get away with the deception, she covered my dark hair and most of my face with a scarf. Father, in another car, pretended to be an Armenian, a deception that had worked well in

Russian during the Bolshevik Revolution.

I felt hot and breathless in the railroad car, but Mother insisted that it would be too dangerous for people to see my olive complexion. The ruse was for me to pretend that I had a cold. I was supposed to cough once in a while, but not too much, because we didn't want to make people move away from us. It would be dangerous to be isolated.

As I snuggled next to Mother and coughed dutifully, I wondered if Commander Igor would wake up at dawn to check the gate for our bodies.

CHAPTER THIRTY-FIVE

We reunited at the Warsaw Railroad Station, where Mother thought it was safe enough to remove my scarf. Ah, finally I could breathe! Feeling liberated, I unbraided my hair and shook it out. Mother was horrified that my dark hair would cast suspicion, but no one was paying attention.

"All right everyone," Father said. He took out the street map that Commander Igor had provided us, along with a list of streetcar schedules and transfers. "It's a pre-war map, and in it all the buildings are intact."

Not so in real life. From the streetcar we observed the ruins of Warsaw. Some houses were standing, but with knocked-out windows and doors. Others seemed to have the top floor sheered away, as if a giant had slapped the building.

The Warsaw Jewish Committee was housed in the two floors remaining from an originally taller building. We were ushered in to see Mr. Asher Pincus, a pudgy man with rosy cheeks and tufts of grey hair on his dome. His function, according to Commander

Igor, was to find lodgings for displaced refugees. On the wall behind him hung a picture of a man with a dense black beard whose name was Theodor Herzl and who, as I had learned in the Fortress, had predicted that Jews would one day have our own country.

Mother's first question was, "Do you have a list of survivors?"

"Mrs. Rubinow," the man answered, "everyone entering this office asks the same question. Even when they're hungry or have no place to sleep, they first ask me about 'the list.'"

Father put a stop to this banter. "You're right Mr. Pincus. We are hungry and have no place to sleep."

The door to another room opened, and through it we saw people milling around, reading lists mounted on the walls. Mr. Pincus pointed to them. "These are the lists. But I must warn you; most people go away disappointed."

A man scanning the wall noticed us peeking in and ran in, saying incredulously, "Kuba Rubinow!" He grabbed my parents' hands in both of his. "Oh, my God, you are alive! And little Rala, you don't remember me, but I hid under your bed."

"Joseph Kesenbaum!" Father hugged the younger man. "Thank God you survived." Mother touched Mr. Kesenbaum, as if to make sure that he was not an apparition.

"Without you I would have been dead a long time ago," he told the three of us. He was younger than Father and of medium height, dressed in a well-cut suit, with a shirt and tie. So this is what an elegant man looks like!

"Please, Mr. and Mrs. Rubinow!" Mr. Pincus' voice rang out.

Quickly Joseph Kesenbaum gave us his card. "My main office

and residence are in Lodz, but I have a small office in Warsaw. And when in Warsaw I come here."

We promised to be in touch as soon as we were settled, and he walked out of Mr. Pincus' office.

"The best and safest place for a family is Dzierzoniow, the former German city Reichenbach," Mr. Pincus said. We nodded. He handed us three railroad tickets and some money. "Unfortunately, we have no place for you to stay overnight, so you must head directly to the railroad station and catch the next train." He also gave us money for food and upkeep for the next few days.

With so many Jews in Dzierzoniow, there was no one to fear. Amazingly, the city was not in ruins. Good! I was sick and tired of ruins. Of course, there were Christians here too, many of them German, but we didn't bother with any of them, or they with us.

We moved into a two-bedroom apartment on the second floor of a four-story building. Father had to find work quickly, because the local Jewish Committee offered help for only a week.

It was paradise! I had my own room with my own cot, a bookcase, a big box in which I kept my small wardrobe, and under it my beloved stamp collection, which I expected to grow now that we were permanently settled. Father ardently converted to the Socialist Zionist party, SZ for short. They liked him and his bookkeeping skills, and installed him as their General Secretary.

Mother, meanwhile, continued with her annoying remarks. "Too bad you didn't become a Zionist before the war when my sister begged you to buy an orchard in Palestine."

Father's new strategy was to ignore her. It was becoming obvious that after the threat from the Bialystok police, my parents liked each other even less than before.

It was September, officially autumn, with pleasantly mild weather. For the first time in almost a year, I was back in school. It was a Jewish school, with instruction in Yiddish. Oy! I could speak Yiddish, but didn't know the alphabet. For the first time I learned to write in the opposite direction, that is, from right to left. I was also told that Hebrew, the language of Palestine, had the same alphabet. I was very proud because now I knew three alphabets, Polish, Russian and Yiddish.

Malka was my new best friend, and I was struggling with the question of whether or not I considered her a replacement for Bracha, who, thank God, had survived the train ride. With Bracha, I had asked myself if she was a replacement for Svetya and Masha. No, I decided, no person is a replacement for another person. I have never changed my mind on that.

I loved Malka's crazy black curls that glistened beautifully, but smelled bad. Malka said it was because her mother used mayonnaise to wash her hair. "I told her no more mayonnaise, and she promised to wash my hair with egg yolks."

"So you'll have to eat the egg white without the yolks."

We laughed.

Then one day, disaster. Malka showed up in school crying, because soon her family would relocate to another formerly German city, Wroclaw. I was despondent after Malka left, and tried to avoid becoming friendly with anyone. There was no point to it. In Poland, everyone moved so fast that friendship would only break your heart.

On January 3, 1947, I turned eleven. Mother kissed me and said, "On February 11, Wowka will be twenty-one."

But before this date, we received a strange letter from my brother. The return address was a Red Army post office box in the Soviet Union, not in Germany. "Mama, I miss you so terribly that I'll die if I don't see you soon. I also miss Father and my dear little sister Rala, who must be all grown up now."

Mother was wiping tears. Father reread the letter, frowning at the last part, which said, "Please contact Samuel Globeichik in Warsaw, who will deliver my personal greetings." There was a telephone number attached.

Angrily Father threw the letter on the table. "Absolutely not! I shall not pay one zloty to get him out of Russia."

Several days went by. We lived in silence, since Wowka's name was not to be uttered, although this was all we were thinking about. One day Mother asked me if I would like to come with her on a visit to her friend Tanya Wisniewska, who lived with her husband in a villa outside the city. I jumped at the opportunity, because I liked their son David.

But that was not where we were headed. Instead, we took the train to Lodz. "We're going to see Joseph Kesenbaum," Mother explained. "He owes me for saving his life, and he must repay me by saving my son."

I had never heard Mother speak so bluntly, because she did not usually believe that a good deed must be repaid.

"You want Mr. Kesenbaum to pay you with money?" I asked.

She averted her face.   "Yes. I spoke with the man Wowka had mentioned in his letter. This kind of transaction means bribing a string of generals and commissars. It is very expensive."

After we arrived in Lodz, we took a streetcar to Mr. Kesenbaum's office. It was pleasant to ride through a city that had not been destroyed. There were many two-story private homes, also apartment buildings and sidewalks with trees. Very pleasant. I wonder why this city was spared when Bialystok and Warsaw were destroyed?

Mr. Kesenbaum's office was on the third floor of a white-washed corner building. The doorplate read: J. Kesenbaum Textiles, Import & Export. It was a nice office, two rooms with shiny new furniture. In the first was a secretary typing; the second was Mr. Kesenbaum's.

Mother and Mr. Kesenbaum shook hands. The atmosphere was a little strained. Still, I did not expect hysterics so soon. But right after the greeting, Mother burst in tears and fell on her knees before Mr. Kesenbaum. I was so embarrassed that I walked over to the window and pretended to watch the traffic.

The sobbing stopped, and I turned around. Mother was standing again. "You must understand the terrible thing that happened to Wowka. The NKVD forced him to stay in Germany, because he had taught himself the language, and they needed him. You surely remember how brilliant he is. I was given to understand that this is the last opportunity to bring him back."

Mr. Kesenbaum asked his secretary to bring Mother a glass of water. Then he asked, "How much?"

He did not faint when Mother mentioned the sum. "Mrs. Rubinow. I owe you my life, and I won't disappoint you. Somehow I'll raise the money."

With that we left and headed back to the railroad station. When we returned to Dzierzoniow we told Father that Tanya Wisniewska sent her regards.

CHAPTER THIRTY-SIX

On a crisp morning in March, Wowka Rubinow jumped off the train onto the platform where his parents and little sister waited. Each of us three had a separate set of emotions. Mother was the happiest.

Wowka grabbed Mother and lifted her up in the air. Both of them cried. "I missed you so much, Mama!"

It was such a wonderful sight that I also cried. After all, it had been four years. Father and Wowka shook hands. My brother lifted me up in the air and gave me a big kiss on the way down.

"Hey, Ralka, you grew! Though not by much." Now both of us were laughing. Same old Wowka.

He had also grown, not by much, but now he was taller than his father. And he looked splendid, well fed. His hair was long, a twisted mop of ash blond, and, with his blue eyes, his resemblance to Mother was unmistakable.

Mother bought food before we left for the railroad station. We sat down to a supper of omelets with yellow cheese, rye bread and cucumber salad, followed by a cup of tea.

Wowka ate everything, and Mother's smile was proof of her delight to be reunited with her son. I showed Wowka my room, with my primitive bookcase and my very own writing desk. He said that he was impressed.

"And look how my stamp collection grew!" I turned the pages, most of them filled.

"Bravo, Ralka, you have become a true cosmopolitan."

After the meal, Wowka picked up his rucksack and put it in my room. I went from happy to livid. "Absolutely not! This is my room, and I shall not give it to you! Mine, mine, mine!"

I walked over and grabbed his rucksack. It was too heavy to lift.

Father sipped his tea, while Mother tried to calm me down. "Rala, remember what he went through in the army. Give him the room for a few nights, and then we'll see."

Before I could burst out again, Father stood up. "Wowka, you will sleep on the couch in the living room."

"But it's too short for him," Mother protested.

"Then we'll bring a chair where he can put his feet. Discussion closed."

I won!

The next day, Father took Wowka to a storage building owned by his Socialist Zionist party. They returned with a long mattress. Grumbling about his suffering, Wowka slept on the mattress on the living room floor.

Later in the week, after Father had left for work, Wowka said, "You know that I was wounded in the war?

Mother's hand flew to her mouth. "Oh, my God, show me

where."

"It's not what you think. My injuries are more severe than blood. I think I should tell you about it."

I begged to listen, and Mother agreed to let me stay out of school to hear my brother's story. He pointed to his left eye. "See the tears in the corner of my eye?" We nodded. "As you know, I'm too tall for the infantry." Wowka walked over to the cabinet and found Father's bottle of cognac, of which only a third was gone.

Mother was appalled. "Wowka it's morning! It's too early to drink."

"It's never too early or too late for a Red Army soldier to have some alcohol." He poured himself half a glass, corked the bottle, but did not return it to the cabinet. "To continue. Because of my height, the general recommended me for a scouting unit. It was also because I had told them that I speak German. The truth, of course, is that I speak Yiddish, but even Russian generals are ignorant muzhiks. I must add that shortly after I became a scout, I taught myself real German.

"In April 1944, I found myself in charge of three other scouts, tall enough, but shorter than me. We received intelligence that the Germans had withdrawn from a certain village, and our brigade was ordered to occupy it. As a precaution, the general dispatched my boys and me to check it out."

Wowka took a handkerchief out of his pocket and wiped his tears. "Darkness was setting in, and the village appeared quiet. We moved closer and were shocked to see that the Germans were still there, slowly packing up. Clearly, I had to do something fast."

Wowka stretched his hand toward the bottle, but changed his mind. "On our way in, we passed a frozen lake. However, since this was April, we guessed that water had already accumulated under the top layer of ice. No choice but to jump into the lake. There was water, icy water. I stared at the Germans through my binoculars and saw them sweeping their barracks. Fucking Krauts! Excuse me, Mama and Ralka. Cleaning up when their army had killed thousands. I assured my soldiers that our stay in the lake would be short."

This time he uncorked the bottle and poured himself another half glass. "But I was wrong about predicting the German departure. As if tired from the cleaning, the Germans settled for the night. In the end, I spent eighteen hours in the frozen lake, with water up to my chest. The others, shorter than I, were dead." He took a gulp of cognac. "A doctor in Berlin told me that my immune system is in bad shape, since I suffered significant damage to my tear ducts and sinuses."

I felt sorry for him, but not enough to relinquish my room.

In the salon where Wowka slept, he tacked onto the wall the picture of a very pretty girl. Shiny dark brown hair, a big smile and painted eyebrows.

"Your girlfriend?" I asked.

"I wish. She's a German actress called Marika Rak. Starred in many Nazi films. I wonder what happened to her."

One day I returned early from school and found Wowka in the salon kissing a very pretty girl, large in the chest and cheeks with too much rouge. Her skirt was lifted and her long legs exposed. The bedroom door was closed, which meant that Mother was inside lying in the dark, not seeing, and pretending not to hear. Lying in a darkened room had become Mother's new, worrisome habit.

"This is my sister Ralka, and this is my friend Karola," Wowka said when he saw me.

Karola pulled down her skirt and smiled too broadly. I went into my room. Soon I heard the front door close, which meant that Wowka and Karola had left. I did not disturb Mother, not wanting for her to be embarrassed.

That day in school I had concluded a significant stamp trade: my Palestinian stamp of King George, for Frumke's Australian with a mama kangaroo and her baby in a pouch. Now I reached under my pile of clothes and felt emptiness. I tossed away the clothes to make sure. My stamp collection was gone. And I knew where it went!

I shouted, "Mama, your son is the lowest human being on earth! He is a one-cell amoeba."

I was immediately sorry for making a fuss after promising myself not to disturb Mother. But it was too late. She came out of the bedroom, eyes glistening with tears.

"It's a mistake, Mama, don't worry about it. Maybe I left my stamp collection in school."

After we finished dinner, I said, "Wowka, come to my room for a minute so I can show you the picture of my beautiful teacher."

He did, and I closed the door and tried to whisper. "You idiot. You stole my stamp collection. It's mine and I want it back."

He laughed. "I gave it to Karola, and believe me it was worth it. Ralka, we both know that you are not a real stamp collector. It's something to do, like collecting dolls."

I forgot my noble intentions and yelled at him. "Only a hooligan would steal his little sister's stamp collection."

My yelling brought Father into my room. He slapped Wowka across the face, not once but twice. "Tomorrow morning you will get out of my house, and never return. I don't care what your mother did to get you out of Russia, but I am ordering you out of here.'"

In the morning, Wowka threw his belongings in his rucksack and banged the door behind him. Mother fell on the sofa, sobbing. Wordlessly, Father took my hand and escorted me to school. He had never done this before, but he must have guessed that without him I would have stayed home to comfort Mother.

When I returned home from school, I noticed that the only reminder of Wowka's stay was the picture of the German actress on the wall.

Shortly afterward, blood started coming between my legs. I was worried, because I figured this was an indication that soon I would die. I told Mother about it, and she looked at me with distaste. "That's all I need now! I'm sorry, Rala, but it's too early. And no, you're not going to die."

She smiled. Then we sat down and she explained to me about my period, and that it came once a month and lasted several days, sometimes with pain, and that she would give me some of her cotton for the blood.

Two weeks after Wowka's banishment, we received a letter from him addressed to "Estera Rubinow and Rala." "Spectacular news! I am in Lodz, where I have been accepted to the newly established Motion Picture Program at the Polish Academy of Fine Art, which will give me a university degree in directing movies. I received excellent grades in all my entrance exams. The school provided me with a Leica camera, so I can take pictures whenever I want. And the next semester our visiting professor will be Umberto Barbaro and Vittorio de Sica."

Mother cried with joy. I was happy that Wowka was no longer Father's responsibility, though not sure if we should show him the letter.

As it turned out, there was no time for it. In the middle of our elation about Wowka, Father burst into the apartment earlier than normal. He sat heavily at the kitchen table and covered his face with his hands.

"I must get out of Poland immediately," he said. "Within the next twenty-four hours, if possible." We looked at him in shock. He continued, "The Bialystok police tracked me down, and there is an order for my arrest because of our attempt to sell Tanya Rakowski's house. Thankfully, the Party has good connections and are trying to arrange for me a speedy departure."

Disregarding our shock, Father went on, "The party is preparing documents for me under a fictitious name. Tomorrow I will take a train to Warsaw, and from there to Vienna. They will arrange a job for me with the underground railroad, where we smuggle Jews from Austria to France, and from there on boats to Palestine."

"What about us?" I asked, since Mother seemed too petrified to speak.

"The Party won't allow me to take you with me at this time, but they assured me that soon it will be possible for you to join me. In the meantime, I have made excellent arrangements for you with the Party's help. They will relocate you to Lodz, where they have an apartment waiting for you. Rala will go to school, just like here, and you, Fira, will be given a job at the Jewish Community Center."

Father opened his attaché case and handed Mother a felt pouch filled with zlotys.   "Since the party will take care of everything, this is for your personal expenses."

Then Father hugged Mother for longer than ever before, and looked deep into my eyes.

"Rala, I promise, this will be a very short separation."

Then he was gone.

CHAPTER THIRTY-SEVEN

"This is not my recollection of the telephone call I had with your husband, Mrs. Rubinow," said Secretary of the Socialist Zionists in Lodz.

His name, Itsik Kantor, was written on a piece of cardboard mounted on his desk. He reminded me of Dima, because his left arm was missing, the empty sleeve held with a safety pin under his elbow.

I was curious. "Did you lose your arm fighting the Nazis?"

"Rala, please…"

"It's all right, Mrs. Rubinow. Yes, Berlin, with the Red Army. It was worth it."

Mother would not allow idle talk. "But we are here, Comrade Itzik, so what are we supposed to do? My husband assured us that the party promised to provide us with an apartment here in Lodz."

He looked at our suitcase, the last one of the fine leather luggage we had taken with us from Bialystok. "Mrs. Rubinow, what we promised your husband was to take care of you, which did not exactly mean an apartment. But now that I see you both, I shall try my best. On my Zionist honor."

Mother sank into her chair, deflated. Her moods and ability to act had been changing so fast lately that I felt the need to step in.

"What about now? Mother and I must go somewhere."

"Mrs. Rubinow, you can stay for a few days at our adult shelter on Piotrkowska Avenue, and I am sure that your little girl will be happy with children her age at our Children's Home."

Mother recovered. "You mean an orphanage?"

I became angry. "I am not an orphan, and I don't want to go to an orphanage!"

"But you can't be on the street, for God's sake!" With his right hand, Comrade Itzik pushed his blondish hair out of his eyes. "Very well, here is what we'll do. Temporarily, you and your daughter can both stay at the shelter. Do you have any money?"

Seeing Mother's hesitation, I said, "We have no money."

Itzik withdrew a handful of crumbled zlotys out of his pocket. "Fortunately, summer vacation has just begun, so we don't have to worry about school until September."

It was very warm outside, and we were sweating. The refugee habit was so ingrained in us that we wore as much clothing as we could whenever we moved from one place to another.

Waiting for the streetcar, I whispered, "Mama, no one must know about the money that Father gave us."

The streetcar deposited us at the shelter in time for supper, which consisted of noodle pudding and a glass of milk. Mother held on to my hand, and I read what she was thinking: We are still together and will not go to sleep on an empty stomach.

The people around us were neither young nor old. Truly, I had seen so many strangers in the last few months that they had all become a blur, a circle of grey people with indistinct features. These people were drab and sad, resigned to a future they could not fathom. I was sure that there were young and energetic Jews in Lodz, but they did not live in this shelter.

In a long dormitory room, Mother and I were assigned two cots next to each other. We received a towel and a small bar of soap each. We washed up haphazardly, and, moments later, fell asleep.

The next morning we ate a breakfast of tea and black bread with strawberry jam. Mother stared at her plate, aloof, pretending that nothing taking place in this shelter concerned us. We had left our suitcase under the cot, as did the other residents. Mother had a large brown handbag from the American shipments, and I carried my schoolbag with a notebook, a pencil and a napkin holding slices of bread we had snatched from the breakfast table.

We found out the address of the Film Institute where Wowka was a student, and took a streetcar in that direction. The Film Institute was beautiful, housed in a solid pre-war structure. We walked through the gate and into a large courtyard surrounded by a bounty of green lawns and trees. Mother approached one of the young men milling around, and asked if he knew student Wlodzimierz Rubinow.

"Oh, yes, everyone knows Wowka."

Proudly, she said, "I am his mother, and this is his little sister, Rala."

Wowka was located and was soon walking toward us, his face registering consternation. He wore a navy jacket and a multicolored scarf draped casually around his neck. He hugged and kissed us both.

"Your father was called on a secret mission to smuggle Jews into Palestine, so his party, the Socialist Zionists, is taking care of us," Mother informed.

"Son of a bitch," Wowka cursed in Russian. "He abandoned you, pure and simple, and I don't know why you keep defending him." He looked at his nice wristwatch. "I must run, or I'll be late for my next class. And, Mama, Rala, next time you visit, could you wear something nicer?" He blew us a kiss and ran away.

The shelter's director was Dr. Witold Ostrowski, formerly a cardiologist with a popular practice in Lodz. Now alone, he was caring for people in a different way. When he got to Palestine, he said, he would return to practicing medicine.

Dr. Ostrowski had black hair around his bald pate. I thought that perhaps he darkened the little hair he had. His piercing black eyes matched the darkness of his hair, like a picture of the crazy monk Rasputin I had seen in the Biysk Public Library.

The day after our visit with Wowka, Dr. Ostrowski told us that the law did not allow for children to live in a shelter with adults, because it might be dangerous. Mother assured him that it was only a matter of days before we would move into our apartment. So Dr. Ostrowski compromised. I would be allowed to sleep at the shelter and eat breakfast and supper, but during the day, when Mother worked at the shelter's tailor shop, I had to occupy myself elsewhere.

Before going off to work, Mother packed some bread and jam for me, and also a bottle of water. I told her not to worry, because the Lodz Public Library was only a block away, and I was eager to start reading books. Lovingly I remembered Raisa and Aksinya in Biysk and looked forward to establish a friendship with a librarian or two here in Lodz.

I went in smiling. Another welcoming library! It was familiar territory. I was too old for milk and cookies, but friendship was enough. The librarian, a middle-aged lady in a green dress and black apron, looked at me without interest. I waited a while at her desk, but she refrained from looking at me. Still, I needed help with a book.

"Good morning, Madam Librarian," I said at last. "Could you please help me find a book?"

"What do you like to read?"

"I love Polish writers, and also stories about history."

She walked over to a nearby shelf and came back with the thickest book I had ever read. It was Quo Vadis, by Henryk Sienkiewicz. I thanked her and wondered why she was staring at me with displeasure. I took the book to a table near a far wall, trying to make myself invisible.

I opened the book, somehow unable to read. So I sat there turning pages. What was bothering me most was Wowka's claim that Father had abandoned us. I remembered the scene he had caused in Petrovna's house the night the NKVD came to take Father into the Red Army, but ended up taking them both. I remembered his telling us that once upon a time, before I was born, Mother had a Polish lover. It was an awful burden he had put on our parents and me for the rest of our lives. So why should I trust my brother now? Maybe Father really had to leave that night. And yet…

I would try to make more sense of it later. But first, to the book. Quo Vadis is a story about people who lived in ancient Rome. They wanted to become Christians, but Christianity was illegal—this was news to me!—and they were persecuted for it. I looked at the librarian's sour face and thought that at least she deserved to be persecuted. It would take me days to read this mammoth book.

The next day I learned from the book that Christians who wanted to introduce themselves to other Christians, made the sign of a fish. But when the Romans caught any of them, they put them in the arena, which is a huge round space, and encouraged lions to eat them.

Back to thinking about the possibility of our abandonment. The previous night I had a brand new and most disturbing thought: It was Mother, not Father, who tried to sell her brother's building. Father was not a blood relative, and would not be permitted to sign the papers. Only Mother. She was the one who swore before a magistrate that she was Tanya Rakowski. So why on earth would the police chase Father instead of the real criminal?

Mother was still too fragile to answer these questions. I would put them to her sometime in the future, when she felt better. I kept on reading about the misfortunes of Christians. Nearly reaching the end of the novel, I wondered how I could persuade the vinegary librarian to give me a shorter book. Anything by Russian authors was out of the question. The country was Communist, but Poles hated Russians more than ever.

At supper, Mother said that the tailor shop had assigned her to sew men's shirts. "It's worse than brassieres. It's slave labor, and they pay us slave wages." At that rate, I thought, there might never be a good time to ask her if she thought that Father had abandoned us.

A few women came in crying hysterically. They had heard rumors that the British had built concentration camps for Jews on the island of Cyprus, where they forced them to take showers. Pandemonium descended on the dining hall. It took Dr. Ostrowski's loud voice to calm them down. "Yes, the British have built detention centers on Cyprus. As everyone knows, soon we shall have a Jewish state, and the detainees will be moved there. As far as the showers are concerned, I swear that they are to clean you, not kill you."

As in Bialystok, Mother and I did not have an address. Still, she wrote a glowing letter to her sisters, and asked me to add my personal greetings.

First, I read her letter. "My dear beloved Zila and Mina, we have moved to the city of Lodz, which, as you know, has not been destroyed by the Nazis because it's a profitable commercial center. It is a highly civilized place with lush gardens and expansive boulevards. The reason for our move was Kuba's promotion to Secretary General of the Socialist Zionist Party in Lodz. We live in a lovely apartment on a street with trees, near Rala's school. Wowka is also in Lodz, and we are very proud of him. He is the best student in the Polish Film University. We are very happy, so there's no need to be concerned about us."

I looked at Mother angrily. "Mama, these are lies! What are you trying to achieve? Why didn't you write the truth, so they could send us money, or help us to get out of here?"

"No, Father will get us out of here. He promised. And I'm not about to whine before my sisters and tell them what has become of us."

No, she does not even admit to herself what Father had done to us. Here's what I wrote to my aunts: "My dear aunts Zila and Mina, I love you very much and hope to be with you soon. Kisses, Rala."

"That's all? You usually have more to say."

"Today I have little to say."

Another letter sent to Palestine without a return address. At some future point, Mother would probably claim that she had forgotten to add it.

A couple of weeks later, Dr. Ostrowski handed us a letter from Itzik Kantor's office. It was from Father, the first letter we had received since his departure. "Dear Fira and Rala," it read, "How are you? I checked with the Party leaders in Poland, and they assured me that you have been given an apartment and are very comfortable. I am so busy with leading refugees from Czechoslovakia and arranging for their passage to France. It's so busy that I have little time to sleep. Also, I don't live in an apartment per se, but in a room in a local pension, which is why I cannot bring you here just yet. But whatever happens, we Jews will soon have a state in which we shall be reunited. Your loving husband and father, Kuba."

Mother threw the letter into her handbag without saying a word. I reread it twice to make sure that Father had no intention of bringing us to Austria. Yes, one way or another, we would be going to Palestine.

Next day in the library, I didn't dare return Quo Vadis, choosing instead to spend another day with martyred Christians. To gain the librarian's friendship, I memorized two pages that appeared to me as poetic. I recited them to her. She looked puzzled. "How on earth can you remember this?" she asked. No point in doing anything like this again.

The following day another librarian joined Number One. She was taller and had a huge behind, and was not likely to be seduced by my recitation of pages from Quo Vadis, either. At the end of the day I returned Sienkiewicz to Librarian Number Two and asked for a book about the Piast royal dynasty. She stared at me with cold blue eyes. "No one reads books about the Piasts anymore."

"How is it possible?" I asked. "They ruled Poland till the fifteenth century." As soon as I spoke the words, I knew I shouldn't have. I fully expected to be thrown out of the library.

But I was lucky. She handed me a book by the Polish writer, Alexander Prus, called Pharaoh, about people more ancient than the Romans, and a time long before Jesus died on the cross. I knew nothing about Egypt and had no desire to find out. But since the only place for me to spend my days was the library, I sat in the corner with Pharaoh on my desk.

Hey, not bad! I liked the barges sailing up and down a river called the Nile. Slaves fanning rich people as they reclined, undoubtedly eating delicious food.

When I was ready to leave for the day, I returned the book to Number Two. "Thank you for suggesting this book."

CHAPTER THIRTY-EIGHT

By that time we had lived in the shelter for almost two weeks and knew that soon our time would be up. One evening after supper, Dr. Ostrowski spoke to us in private.

"Mrs. Rubinow, Rala, you cannot remain here any longer. This is against the law, and if someone talks, we may lose our license." Though expected, it was a blow. "Look, you can return in two weeks' time, and we'll try to do this again. But Rala cannot return here tomorrow evening."

Back to Comrade Itsik. "Mr. Kantor," Mother said, spreading Father's letter in front of him. "You do read Russian, and can see for yourself that the Party directors have assured my husband that we have already been given an apartment."

Itzik Kantor scanned the letter and sighed. "I have not spoken with your husband personally, and I have received no communication from anyone in the leadership." He was unshaven, with dark circles under his eyes. This man really had had little sleep. But he tried hard to be friendly.

"I am incredibly sorry. I promise that I shall try to get you two permanent lodgings. In the meantime, have Rala go into the Children's Home. School will start soon, and once there, she will be immediately enrolled."

Had Mother accepted, I would have agreed, albeit reluctantly.

"This child is not an orphan," she responded. "She has a mother, and I don't want her to be known as an orphan."

Mother asked for a Lodz telephone book. She scanned some pages, took a piece of paper and a pencil out of her handbag, and jotted something down. Then she waved at the Secretary and pulled me out of the room, carrying our fine, pre-war suitcase.

Where were we going to sleep? My stomach cramps intensified, but I said nothing, used to the fact that whenever I was nervous or scared, my stomach paid the price. When Mother was extra nervous, she would complain of a migraine.

Back on the avenue, we located a public bench and sat down. I was sorry about Mother's carrying the suitcase, and though I knew that there was little in it, it was too large for me to handle.

"What was the note you made from the telephone book?"

"Mr. Kesenbaum's address."

"Oh, no, not again! Not after what he did for Wowka!"

"We can't be particular. Either we go to him, or we sleep on this bench." She was obviously quite agitated, so I just nodded and smiled. She took a mirror and a lipstick out of her handbag and colored her lips, then dabbed her cheeks with a little bit of the lipstick. She proceeded to comb her hair and straighten my braids.

"You look very pretty, Mama."

"And so does my daughter."

We climbed the streetcar and asked the conductor to announce our stop. Then we got off in front of an imposing three-story building, the outside walls so clean, they must have been scrubbed. We rang the bell and were ushered into the building by a doorman, who announced us on the telephone. Then he said, "Second floor."

We dragged our suitcase upstairs. "Don't interrupt me, no matter what I say," Mother whispered.

The Kesenbaums occupied the entire second floor. We rang the bell, and Mr. Kesenbaum opened, looking at us in amazement.

"Oh, Mr. Joseph!" Apparently, Mother was resolved to prevent him from asking any questions, because she didn't let him get a word in. "Rala and I have just arrived from Dzierzoniow. You know that Kuba became an important figure in the Zionist movement and was suddenly dispatched on a secret mission to Austria to smuggle Jews to Palestine. His party, the Socialist Zionists, are fixing up an apartment for us. So we wondered if maybe we could stay with you for a couple of nights?"

Oh, my God, was I blushing? I stood next to Mother, my eyes fixed on the high-gloss floor, similar to the one back home on which I used to fall and hiccup.

When I raised my eyes, Mr. Kesenbaum was embracing Mother. A maid older than Mother took our suitcase. She had grey ringlets and wore a black dress and white apron.

"This is Melvina," said Mr. Kesenbaum, "My wife's name is Genia, but she is out at a charity meeting. Melvina will make you comfortable in the guest room and prepare some supper."

Melvina smiled, as did Mr. Kesenbaum.

"I have some work to finish in my office," he said, and walked into another room. Melvina showed us a room larger than any we had seen since our apartment in Bialystok. The ceiling was high, and a white lace curtain fluttered at the open window.

Mother smiled at the sight of the large canopied bed, but I had no recollection of ever seeing one. The bedspread was embroidered with rose petals, and the pillowcases with ruffles. Mother and I were in dreamland. Left alone, we gingerly opened a door and found a bathroom like in American movies, with a tub and toilet and soft white paper, fluffy clean towels, and beautifully smelling soap. We must have had all this sometime in the past. Tears in Mother's eyes proved that she remembered the enormity of her loss and the misery of our present condition.

A knock on the door announced the arrival of Mrs. Kesenbaum. Genia was pretty, with a smiling pink mouth and a big behind. She wore a white dress with dainty red roses embroidered on it.

We washed our hands and were invited to the dining room. The main dish was a moist chicken with mushrooms, which Mother and I ate slowly, so as not to display how starved we were. How long would this last? With our luck, not long.

Before going to sleep, we took long baths and washed our hair.

The next morning, I disregarded Mother's instructions to eat little, and filled up with breakfast food to last me through the day. The Kesenbaums watched me, but I didn't care. When we finished, Mother said that on her way to work, she would drop me off at school. It's a good thing they didn't inquire about my book bag and school supplies. Possibly, Mr. Kesenbaum saw through Mother's deception about Father's "important" mission. Stupid people don't usually become so rich so fast.

Outside Mother looked deflated, tired of the lies she had concocted. "Can you go back to the library?"

I shrugged. "Now that school has started, it's only a matter of days before they throw me out. But I'll try it today."

We stopped at a bakery and looked in the display window at lovely rolls and tarts. Mother took a few zlotys, a remnant of the money Father had given us before he left. With it we bought two buttered rolls in two separate bags. Into my bag she added a round cookie with a dollop of jelly.

On the way to the streetcar, Mother recognized a tall man in a beautiful camel hair coat.

"Oh, my God!" she exclaimed. "Haim Kagan, thank God you're alive! Rala, this is Haim, Uncle Grisha's younger brother."

The tall man tried not to blink. "Sorry, Madam, but you are mistaking me for someone else. I am Mieczyslaw Boleslawski, and I'm in a rush to get to work." He walked away, accelerating his long strides.

Mother and I ran after him. It would feel great to spit in his face.

"Look at me, Haim," Mother shouted in the kind of loud voice you normally don't use on the street. "I am Esther Rakowski, your Jewish sister-in-law!"

He was so scared of us that he ran, then jumped onto a moving streetcar. We laughed and slapped each other's backs.

Somehow, I lasted in the library till late afternoon. But on my way out, Number One said angrily, "Child, tomorrow you must bring your mother or father, so we know you have a home and did not escape from some institution."

Next morning after breakfast, Genia went on errands, and her husband stayed behind. Here it comes: the talk about us not being able to stay with him forever.

"Mrs. Rubinow," he began, "my very dear friend, Naftali Meister, needs help in his home. He lives in a beautiful apartment not far from here, with his son Peter, who is Rala's age." Mother blinked. "Naftali owns a fine jewelry store where he spends his working days, but he needs someone to keep house and cook supper. It would be a wonderful place for you both. You will have a nice room with your own bath, great food, and a warm family." Pause. "And of course, he will pay you a salary, though I cannot say how much."

My mother, Esther Rakowski Rubinow, was being asked to become a servant. She stood up and extended her hand. "Thank you, Joseph, I'll take it."

Giving us no time to think, Mr. Kesenbaum carried our suitcase outside and hailed a taxi. I realized with some excitement that this would be my first taxi ride ever. As Mother stepped in after me, Mr. Kesenbaum gave the driver the address and some bills.

CHAPTER THIRTY-NINE

The taxi brought us to another beautiful building on the same avenue. The structure consisted of three floors of reddish brick. A staircase from the street led to a first floor apartment, Mr. Meister's.

"Mrs. Rubinow and Rala, so happy you are here." He grabbed our suitcase and jauntily ran up the stairs. He was short but trim, with spiky salt-and-pepper hair and black-rimmed glasses, the kind I liked in men.

The foyer was medium-sized, but the salon was gigantic, with a fluffy sofa of bluish-gray and two armchairs, each half the size of the sofa, made of the same fabric. Everything was neat and pleasant; even the drapes were ironed. So why did Mr. Meister need my mother to keep his house in order?

"You have an onion," I told Mr. Meister, and Mother laughed. She charmingly explained how old Major Rosstovsky hunted in our apartment for these round old watches.

"I sell them in my jewelry store."

The dining room table was laid out with milk and cookies for me, and tea for Mr. Meister and Mother.

"It is an honor to have you here, Mrs. Rubinow," our host said kindly. "Joseph told me about your illustrious rabbinic family."

He looked at Mother, as if astonished that she was so pretty. I helped myself to another cookie.

Then he showed us to our room. Two beds with a small table in the middle, a closet with hangers, and a chest of drawers.

"You'll share the bathroom only with my son Piotrek, whose bedroom is next to yours."

He patted me on the head.

"Ladies, it is very important that you call me Natek, which is short for Naftali. Now I shall leave you and go pick up Piotrek from school."

We unpacked, luxuriating in our new accommodations, which were even nicer than Mr. Kesenbaum's guest room. I took a shower and thought of Piotrek, the bathroom's owner. I had been minus a friend since Malka in Dzierzoniw, so maybe Piotrek would be my new friend.

Natek's icebox was huge, with two blocks of ice. In it we found every sort of vegetable and fruit, meats, cheeses and eggs. Mother began preparing the evening meal, and I was eager to help.

Natek and Piotrek returned around four p.m. Piotrek and I examined each other with the utmost curiosity. Piotrek had the same spiky hair as Natek, but his was black. He wore thick glasses, but without the black frames. He had a rigidly pressed knicker suit, but no onion.

Mother worked miracles in the kitchen. We made a lettuce salad with sliced tomatoes and cucumbers. The fried chicken was juicy and tender, and the mashed potatoes had real butter. And strawberries with sour cream for dessert. No words to express my delight.

"Tomorrow there will also be soup," Mother announced proudly.

"Mrs. Rubinow," Natek began.

"Please call me Fira."

"Fira, of course. We have a cleaning woman twice a week who will continue to come in, so you don't have to perform work unbefitting a lady."

The next evening Mother made a barley soup with milk call krupnik in Polish.

"I have never eaten a soup so tasty," Piotrek announced. His father beamed.

"Do you want to play checkers?" I offered.

"Yes, but only after I finish my homework."

Natek registered me in the same Polish school that Piotrek attended, and into the same grade. He bought me a rucksack, not with leather straps like Piotrek's, but spacious enough to carry the books and notebooks he gave me.

Each morning, Natek took Piotrek to school in a taxi. He invited me to join them, but Piotrek said, "No, it's my taxi."

I said I didn't mind, and that I loved riding the streetcar. I told myself that I would not impose myself into the habits that Natek and his son had developed. They were not so important to me.

My knowledge of subjects was uneven, because I had never stayed in any school for an entire year. But I read a lot, and I knew about history and literature more than the others. My weakness was arithmetic, and in biology I knew zero. I remembered that at one point in the past my father had been a mathematics teacher. A very unsuccessful mathematics teacher, at that.

Rala needs help! My solution: Find someone two or three grades above to tutor me in arithmetic and biology without pay. Must be a boy, because girls were not good in these subjects. I roamed the corridors, checking out the older Jewish boys. A Christian would not only refuse to teach me, but would probably beat me up.

Then I spotted someone I thought might be a candidate. He was tall, maybe as tall as Wowka, in a long coat, and he had a confident smile. I found out that his name was Marek Halter, and that he was smart.

"Marek," I said, approaching him one day, "I am Rala Rubinow. I am new here, and I already missed two months. So I very much need help in arithmetic and biology."

I said it all in one breath, and he laughed. "This is a joke, right?"

"No. I really need help."

"But I don't like the subjects you want me to teach you. I write stories I make up, and someday I'll write books and become famous."

"But before you become famous, you must teach me arithmetic and biology."

Marek agreed, because there was no other way to get rid of me. Since we both traveled by streetcar, we stayed for a while after classes, and he taught me what I so desperately needed. After a couple of weeks, I caught up with my class, but Marek and I remained friends. Whenever Piotrek saw us together he shook his head, not knowing what to make of it. I often dreamed that Marek was my brother, seeing as I had not seen my real brother since our last and only visit to the Polish Film Academy.

In class, my best subject was poetry. We were studying Maria Konopnicka, one of Poland's most beloved poets, and my personal favorite. I stayed up late to make sure that my homework was perfect.

Piotrek asked, "Rala, why do you study so hard?"

"Because I don't want anyone to get ahead of me."

"But why?"

I had to stop and think. Really, why?

"Because you cannot be excellent if someone is more excellent than you."

But soon my mind became preoccupied with Mother and Natek instead of my studies. I lay in bed, pretending to sleep, knowing that soon Mother would sneak out and go to the other bedroom to be with him. I could think of two reasons why this was happening, and both of them made sense. First, Mother liked Natek more than she liked Father. It was possible that at this point, she actively disliked Father. Second, we needed this place, the room, the food, Natek, Piotrek—and whatever came with it.

During this time, a breezy letter arrived from Father, delivered by Mr. Itzik Kantor's secretary. In it was a greeting: "To my dearest Fira and Rala from your loving husband and Father." Attached was a picture of father, smiling broadly, his arms around two pretty young ladies. In the background were tall, snowy mountains, shimmering in what seemed to be late afternoon sun.

Meanwhile, Piotrek's reaction to his father and my mother was subdued fury. I realized that I knew nothing about his dead mother, but had no doubt that he must be thinking of her constantly. I didn't ask, because I preferred not to know. From the moment we had arrived back in Bialystok, I had been inundated by stories about how people died. My family, every Jew in Bialystok, mothers and fathers of the fighters and partisans. Even Father Paul's saints. All of their deaths were nasty and brutal.

In school, I always knew the answers in literature and history classes. But I had to restrain myself or people would accuse me of showing off. Especially Piotrek. One day our literature teacher, Mrs. Dombrowska, assigned as homework Maria Konopnicka's heroic poem about Poland's beloved king Jan Sobieski, who in the seventeenth century defeated the Turks at the gates of Vienna and saved Europe from becoming Moslem. The topic: "Describe how Poland saved Europe."

"Our newcomer, Rachela Rubinowa, received the highest mark, a full five," said the teacher, shaking her head between wonder and dismay.

Lola, a girl with awful pimples, said in a nasal drawl, "Mrs. Dombrowska, why do you give the highest grade to a Jew?" Lola pointed at me. "I think she's a witch."

The teacher did not deny the possibility that I might be a witch. Her comment was, "I'll think about it."

Piotrek ran off at the bell's first chime to meet Natek, who, I knew, had been waiting for him in a taxi. My streetcar station was two blocks away, and as I exited, my classmates were waiting for me. Four boys in front, two girls in the back, one of them pimply

Lola.

One boy yelled, "My father says that the Jews are back to take over our country."

This cretin son of an imbecile kicked me in the stomach with his shoe. I doubled over, but bit my lip not to cry. Lola snatched my bookbag and dumped my books, papers and pencils onto the pavement. They tore my essay with the big red "five" emblazoned on it.

As with all beatings, there was a pause. I used it to grab my possessions off the cobblestones, shove them into my bookbag, and run toward the oncoming streetcar. Inside the car, I stared at the floor, avoiding eye contact with other passengers.

As I jumped off the streetcar in front of Natek's house, I saw a huge white dog walking toward me. Because of the way he was shorn, he looked like a tree at the Lodz Museum. His white mane was fluffy like a dandelion, while the rest of his body was shaven clean, with only a pompom of hair wiggling at the end of his tail. There were similar pompoms on his feet. I thought, Poor animal, whoever you are!

Attached to him was my brother, Wowka Rubinow, grandson of the illustrious rabbi Jacob Meyer Rakowski and a direct descendant of King David. There was a woman next to him, short and dressed in what looked like a coat made of the hair they had shaven off the dog.

Wowka stared at me with surprise. Then he recovered.

"Elsa, this is my sister, Rala."

"Ah little Ralichka! How you have grown!" She hugged me and slobbered my cheek with kisses. Maybe she was more interesting than her dog. "When I last saw you in Bialystok, you were three years old."

Mother must have seen us through the window. She rushed down the stairs.

"Oh, Wowka, I'm so glad you stopped by to visit!" Wowka bent down to kiss our mother. When she looked at the woman with him, she exclaimed, "Oh, my God Elsa Gurevich! I always knew you would get out of there alive. And you look even more like Dolores Del Rio."

Elsa shook her finger at Mother.

"Always my spirited Firochka. But please don't call me 'Gurevich.' It is no longer my name. Now, my name is Markiewicz. My husband is Stefan Markiewicz; you must have heard of him. No? Well, I don't suppose you are in those circles anymore. He is a high trade official in the government, attending a conference in Moscow."

Wowka supplied more information. "Elsa and I met at the preview of the movie "Border Street," directed by Alexander Rom. I was reviewing it for the school newspaper, and Elsa attended as a trustee of the Film School."

"We had a fabulous reunion." Elsa's voice was like scratching an aluminum pot. "That Rubinow height—I would have recognized it anywhere."

"Hey, Mama, you and Ralka live here?"

"Yes, I am governess to Mr. and Mrs. Meister's eight-year-old daughter. It's very convenient. Rala and I have our own small apartment, and she attends the wonderful Polish school on Piotrkowska." My leg hurt, and when I looked down, I noticed that my stocking was torn when I fell after being kicked. I looked back up at them and grinned.

Wowka wrinkled his forehead, as if trying to make sense out of what Mother had told him. He gave up and tugged on the dog's leash.

"Allez, Gaston! You see, Gaston speaks only French. He is a very chic dog. So, au revoir Maman et ma petite soeur." He waved, then he, chic Gaston, and Elsa swooshed down the avenue.

"I didn't know Wowka speaks French."

"He must have taught it to himself," Mother smiled. "You know how smart he is."

"Mama, who is Dolores Del Rio?"

"She is an actress from American movies. She looks like a witch."

CHAPTER FORTY

Sunday morning, Mother wore a gold chain around her neck and on it a disk with small diamonds.

"A gift from Natek," she told me.

I wondered if it had been his wife's. Mother must have guessed my thoughts, because she added, "He brought it for me from his store."

I didn't think Wowka would visit us at a home where Mother was a servant. But one day he arrived just before dinner, dressed in a beautiful black leather jacket. He kissed Mother with unaccustomed exuberance and gave me a peck on the cheek.

"Mama, the smells from the kitchen are divine. You are truly the world's greatest cook!"

Mother beamed at this hypocritical compliment.

"So where are Mr. and Mrs. Meister and their lovely daughter?"

"Well, actually, there is only a Mr. Meister and his son Piotrek, who is Rala's age. A very sweet boy."

Wowka winked. "Good for you, Mama. This is a beautiful

place."

At this moment, Natek and Piotrek came in and curiously stared at Wowka.

"My son," Mother said.

The four of us midgets looked up at my brother.

"Is he adopted?" Natek asked. The joke was good enough to reduce tension.

Piotrek regarded Wowka suspiciously, but being well-mannered, he shook my brother's hand.

"Of course, you will stay for dinner," Natek told him.

We washed up and sat down. Mother brought in the loaf of fresh bread she bought every day at the French bakery, and green salad with lemon and oil dressing. The main course was fried chicken cutlets and macaroni with fried onions. Also, a carrot tzimmes that Natek adored.

"Oh, how nice," said Wowka. "Carrots a la Juif."

"What does that mean?" asked Piotrek.

"Jewish carrots."

"So why don't you just say Jewish carrots?"

I loved Piotrek!

"Whatever you call them, they are great, and I shall have some more," said my brother. I noticed Mother put little on her plate, fearing, of course, that Wowka, eating with abandon, might endanger our standing there.

Usually, at this point in the meal, Mother and Natek drank a cup of coffee. Today she brought coffee only for Natek and Wowka. She carried in three plates with a slice of chocolate cake on each.

"Rala and I don't feel like having dessert," she announced.

I had been looking forward to having the chocolate cake. Piotrek was clearly becoming angrier as the evening progressed. He ate his cake too fast, and asked to be excused.

Wowka was enjoining his coffee. He charmed his host with a smile.

"At this point a little schnapps would feel even better."

Mother jumped. "No, Wowka, we don't have alcohol."

"It's all right, Fira," Natek said quickly. Wowka looked at them, realizing the implication of Natek's calling Mother Fira, a name used only by her family and Father.

Natek proceeded to the cupboard and returned with a bottle of cognac and three glasses. Mother and Natek sipped theirs, but Wowka drained his in two gulps.

As he again reached for the bottle, he said serious tone, "Sometimes I drink too much, but I learned it during my three years in the Red Army. I was in battle from Stalingrad to Berlin."

Predictably, Wowka launched into the story of how he had been trapped in a freezing lake for eighteen hours.

He concluded with the words, "When the frost returns into my bones, a shot of cognac makes all the difference."

Natek was so fascinated that he poured Wowka a third glass, after which Mother replaced the bottle in the cupboard and stood up. So did Natek, then Wowka.

"Please come back soon," Natek said to my brother.

Mother and I led Wowka to the door. She had the courage to say, "Don't walk in on us unannounced. And you cannot come back for two weeks."

We received another letter from Father, again delivered by Itzik Kantor's secretary.

"It is so peaceful and beautiful in Austria, as if the war had never happened," he wrote. "But I am reminded of it every time I escort sad and impoverished refugees from the Czech border to Vienna. I am now leader of the convoys and have more responsibilities than ever. I did take time out for a few days in Vienna to attend a concert by Yehudi Menuhin, though many of my colleagues boycotted him because he had announced that the proceeds would be donated to German orphans. No matter, the music was divine." The letter ended with: "I am so happy that the Party is taking good care of you."

Mother's and Natek's hope that Piotrek and I would become friends was petering out. I felt strongly that I had made every attempt to accommodate him, even to the point of helping him with our written assignments in literature and history. But the more I extended myself, the angrier he became. Not that he screamed or anything like that. But he looked at me with hateful eyes.

Natek was trying to pay me as little attention as possible without being rude. I understood. Natek was as protective of his son as I was of my mother. In Biysk I had my friends Svetya and Masha, and many more when I was permitted to attend school. Here, you prayed not to be hit by Christians, so being friends with them was impossible. Oh, what the hell, I told myself. I'll make friends in Palestine.

"Rala, you must try harder to be nice to Piotrek," Mother told me one day. "He is a sweet boy, he needs a friend."

"I also need a friend."

"There is a difference between your needs and his. People with money have more demands and opportunities. Poor people try harder."

So, what was the name of that university in Paris that I was supposed to attend when Father was rich, and the world was whole?

Then it was Natek's turn to try and improve relations between Piotrek and me by suggesting that we go to the movies together, just the two of us. Natek took us there in a taxi, bought the tickets, and returned home.

"I'll be back in exactly an hour and a half," he said. We nodded. Piotrek had a watch.

The movie was an American comedy. We sat in a dark auditorium, watching. This was the second movie of my life, if you counted "Sun Valley Serenade," of which I saw only half, because the girl in the yellow dress was murdered. In this movie, a pretty blonde girl dressed up as a sailor, so she could slip onto a ship to be with her sailor boyfriend. It was funny. I laughed so hard I got the hiccups. Maybe it was because the Americans are allowed to be funny. The Russians told jokes only in private. Otherwise the NKVD would ship them to the North Pole. And the Poles are unfunny because they have no jokes.

After the movie came a short American newsreel called "Movie tone," about major events around the world. This headline flashed on the screen: "November 29, 1947. The General Assembly of the United Nations, meeting in New York, voted to partition Palestine into a Jewish State and an Arab State." The blue-and-white Jewish flag fluttered in the breeze over a tall building.

Suddenly screams rang throughout the theater. "Jews to

Palestine! Jews to Palestine!"

The screamers were not only teenage hooligans, but also adults. The scary part was that the screams were loudest around us, because Piotrek and I looked Jewish. The teenagers jumped at us through the rows. Unlike Russia, the adults did not protect us.

"Let's run!" I whispered to Piotrek, and we pushed our way toward the back exit. Alas, two of the older hooligans followed. One punched me in the neck, a pause that gave Piotrek an opportunity to run away. But it didn't help, because a second misfit caught up with him and slapped him full force on both cheeks. Piotrek had a nosebleed and a cut lip.

Satisfied, the Poles disappeared. My neck throbbed, but Piotrek's wounds were more visible. We made our way to the front entrance, but it was too early for Natek. The audience was leaving the theatre, so we squeezed behind a corner pillar to avoid another beating.

Ten minutes later, we were rescued by Natek.

Back home, Piotrek cried pitifully, and Mother broke up ice and put it on his face.

"You don't seem to have any wounds," Natek said, looking me over.

"They hit me in the neck." Mother rushed over to me, panic in her eyes.

"Mama, it doesn't hurt too much," I said. "But it would help if you gave me some ice."

The next morning, Piotrek refused to go to school.

"I don't want them to see me like this," he said. I couldn't blame him.

For an essay assignment in school that day, I described my meeting with Elsa's giant poodle, which I called Mr. Twardowski, after a character in a Polish legend caught between heaven and earth.

"This is very funny," said Mrs. Dombrowska. "Read it aloud, Rachel." I did, and the class laughed.

A few days later, Piotrek returned to school, but tried to avoid me. As always, he arrived home in the taxi before me. For dinner, Mother prepared one of Piotrek's favorite dishes—large meatballs called klops, with mashed potatoes and creamed spinach. It was my favorite, too.

I was happily chewing my klops when I heard Piotrek's whiny voice.

"Look Papa, Rala has no table manners." I stopped chewing, ground meat sticking out of my mouth.

"See! Her mouth is full of meat; it's disgusting!"

"Please, Piotrek, stop it," implored his father.

"No, Papa, why do you take her side? You see how she always cuts up the whole klops into pieces, then gobbles it up at once like a rat. Haven't you heard, Rala, that you are supposed to cut only one piece at a time?"

I was burning with rage. Silently I finished chewing what was in my mouth. But Piotrek was not done.

"Papa, you don't know, but everyone in school hates Rala, because she always jumps up first with the answer. You are too miserable to let anyone else answer!" he cried out, turning to me. "You think you're the smartest!"

He stood up, throwing his white cloth napkin on the table, as if challenging me to a duel.

"You clod," I said, also standing up. "I do know more than you. And knowing history and literature is more important than cutting meat the right way."

They stared at me, so I stopped. Piotrek ran to his room, banging the door behind him.

Mother sat down heavily. It took her a few minutes to regain her composure.

"Natek, Rala and I will leave in the morning. I am really sorry it didn't work out."

We went to bed, and Mother held me in her arms all night. In the morning, we packed everything in our suitcase and looked mournfully at each other.

"Rala, eat a big breakfast," she said. "We don't know what will happen next, and we can't take any food with us."

In the kitchen, Mother served Piotrek an omelet with black bread and butter and a glass of chocolate milk. I received the same, eating very slowly, as if I were back in Siberia, salivating over crumbs.

The taxi honked.

"Piotrek," his father said, "please go to school by yourself with Mr. Jerzy. Good manners require that I say good-bye to Mrs. Rubinow."

"I can't go to school any longer," I said mournfully, as soon as the door closed behind Piotrek.

Natek covered his face with his hands. "Oh, my God, if I could only do something."

I retired to our room, but left the door slightly ajar, so I could watch and listen. Natek extended a large stack of money, held together with a rubber band. Mama, please take the money! I beg of you, take the money!

He said, "There is enough here for an apartment and food for at least a month."

Mother pushed it away. "Natek, we'll be fine. As it happens, yesterday I received communication from my husband's Party that they have an apartment ready for us. There is also a good possibility that we shall be on a priority list for a ship to Palestine."

I reappeared in the salon, wearing my coat and hat. She did the same, and Natek took our suitcase into the street. He hailed a taxi and paid the driver.

"Take them wherever they want to go."

CHAPTER FORTY-ONE

"Where to?" asked the driver.

"Drive down the street, so I can speak with my daughter." The driver saluted and did as he was told.

"Rala, we'll go back to the shelter. I am sure that Dr. Ostrowski will take us in for another week, or maybe two."

"And then what? You know that nothing will change. I want to go to the orphanage. All this happened because I spoke harshly to Peter. I'm sorry. I'm tired of the library, and this suitcase. Please Mama, it's for the best."

Her eyes filled with tears, but I could see that she felt relieved. She turned to the driver, "361 Independence Avenue." It was the address of the Zionist Socialist office. What we needed now was an official referral for the orphanage.

At the sight of us, Mr. Kantor blushed behind his beard. Since it was the beginning of December and very cold, he wore a heavy sweater. I noticed that the pin he'd attached to it had a hard time holding up his left sleeve.

As he began stuttering his apologies, Mother interrupted him. "Rala made up her mind to go to your orphanage."

"The Children's Home."

"Whatever you call it. And I shall return to the shelter."

"Mr. Kantor," I said. "Please promise to put us on a priority list to Palestine."

He thought about this for a minute, so maybe his promise had value. "Yes," he said at last. "I'll do my best." He handed us money for both streetcars.

It was already noon, but we convinced ourselves that we were not hungry. Mother stood on the street, hesitating. "First, we must tell Wowka of our change of plans."

"Mama, please forget about Wowka for a while."

"No, it's not what you think. I simply don't want him to show up at Natek's. He called, and I told him to come tomorrow and that I'd make his favorite stuffed cabbage."

Stuffed cabbage. Golubtsi in Russian. Petrovna and Mother cooked it during our last year in Biysk, when conditions were better and we could buy some meat,

Our first streetcar ride was to the Film Institute. No choice but to drag our suitcase into the courtyard, which was already covered with a thin layer of snow.

"Rala will live in the Zionist Children's Home," Mother said, as soon as Wowka emerged into the courtyard.

"Mama, that a euphemism for 'orphanage.'"

"No, it's much nicer. And I will stay at the Party's shelter on Narutowicze."

"Son of a bitch. It's because of your husband that the two of you have been homeless for a year. The scoundrel never forgave you for a minor indiscretion and abandoned you both. But listen, he is in Austria, the smuggling capital of Europe. So tell him to send you dollars. It's the least he can do."

Mother was already sobbing into her handkerchief. Wowka hesitated for a minute. "I swear that I must run to my next class."

"Wowka," I said, "you are a man of exceptional wickedness. I shall pray to God that you be punished for the way you treat your mother." But Wowka was already retreating, and I wasn't sure if he had heard me.

Dragging the suitcase, we found the streetcar that deposited us at the orphanage at 216 Woolczanska Street. It was a filthy industrial neighborhood, where both factories and residences were blackened with soot. The snow looked like salt and pepper, so unlike the immaculate cottony substance surrounding Natek's house.

The orphanage occupied a two-story building. Again, ugly. The director wore a heavy sweater in olive green, and was blond and Aryan-looking. His name was Stefan Grayewski. I already guessed how he had survived. Still, I popped my question.

"Were you in the partisans or the Red Army?"

"Neither. I was on the Aryan side smuggling guns and food into the ghetto. After the ghetto was destroyed, I took the remnant to fight in the Polish Uprising in August of 44."

We had never heard about the Polish Uprising, so he changed the subject. "Let me show you to your bunk."

I was given a top bunk in a room that held about fifteen such beds, which meant that I would be one of thirty girls. I had never slept in a bunk, so I figured it might be interesting. Mother opened the suitcase, and I took out my clothes and toothbrush. My bookbag was filled with school supplies, just in case.

Mother kissed and hugged me at length. Commander Stefan noticed her anxiety. "Mrs. Rubinow, every Sunday the children receive money for a streetcar, so they can go see relatives and friends in the City Park."

Obviously relieved, Mother left, carrying a much lighter suitcase.

The building in which we were housed had been originally divided into apartments. But when the orphanage rented it, permission was given to take down some walls and construct two dormitories, one for girls, and one for boys. The rest of the house consisted of a kitchen, a dining room, and smaller rooms for staff.

There were about fifty of us when I arrived. I told everyone that I was a real orphan, like most of them. In truth, I felt like an orphan, which in my mind was a child that no parent was able or willing to take care of. Though we had plenty of food, people were constantly hungry, myself included. It seemed to be something in our brains, because we had all in the past suffered periods of hunger. And hunger for bread lingers forever.

We were not kosher, because Socialist Zionists don't believe in God. They served a variety of food. In the soup category was chicken soup, barley and pea. Four nights a week, supper was fried chicken with mashed potatoes, twice meatballs, and once a week the great prize: sausage! The desserts were boring, usually chocolate or vanilla pudding.

The children came from all over, meaning that no one knew anyone before they entered the orphanage, with the exception of two brothers, Jessie and Jonathan. Why there were thirty girls, but only twenty boys? Was it because girls were more clever at surviving the war? The girls ranged in age from eight to fifteen. I caught the eye of fifteen-year-old Lucy, who looked very non-Jewish as, upon inspection, did many of the other kids. With my looks I would have never survived the war in Poland.

"I'm Lucy for short," she said, "but my birth certificate says Lucinda. My mother must have gotten it from some romantic novel."

"Is she—?"

"She's dead. But here's what you should know, Rala. We do not ask questions about parents. We don't know who has them and who doesn't. I saw your mother, so you're lucky, but the rest shouldn't be told."

"It's smart."

"I like you already. You catch on fast."

The permanent staff consisted of three. Apart from Stefan was his assistant Debora, a scrappy young woman always in motion, with tiny spectacles and hair that impersonated a neglected broomstick.

"Debora has a memory like a steel tank," Stefan told me when we met.

The third was Berl, maybe as old as forty, with thinning hair, who took care of Socialist-Zionist money. Other than these three, we had no idea who of the adults milling in and out of the building, were our instructors. These young men and women would arrive and stay with us for a week or two, taking us to the park and to the movies, and telling us again and again how we Jews were in exile for two thousand years.

"Poland is exile," they would say. "This room is exile. Everything here is exile. But as soon as we get to Palestine—we shall be out of exile. Forever."

Rumors prevailed about these itinerant young people. The one we believed in was that they were fighters from the Warsaw ghetto and other uprisings, who took an oath to kill as many Germans as possible before sailing to Palestine. They had lists and addresses of Nazis, and when they left the orphanage, they traveled to Germany to kill as many as they could. We were proud of them. We brought them tea with lumps of sugar, and behaved well around them.

The orphans attended the Ghetto Fighters' School, where instruction was in Hebrew, a language I did not know, except for the alphabet, which was the same as in Yiddish. Lucy rode the streetcar with me the first morning. "In school, unlike in the orphanage, most children have either one or both parents, and many of us are jealous, but we don't talk about it. Anyway, I'm not staying after I drop you off because they don't have classes for people my age."

"So, what do you do? Study alone in the library?"

Lucy put her hands on her hips and stuck out her chin. "No, I certainly do not!" Then she walked away.

Our Hebrew teacher, Madame Vogel—no one knew why she insisted on being addressed madame—gave me a Hebrew primer. Difficult language! It didn't sound like anything I'd ever heard, more like the growling of a hungry lion. Not a pretty language, but prettier than Polish.

Good-bye to Polish poets, and hello to Rachel, my namesake, who sang about the beauty of a sea called Galilee; and the writer

Haim Brenner, who suffered like all Russian writers, but in Hebrew. Madame Vogel said that in Hebrew, there are at least half a dozen words for suffering, and that we must learn them all.

The school was located on Poludniowa Street, many streetcar stops from the orphanage. As I was getting accustomed to my new home, I noticed that not all orphans headed to school in the morning, especially the ones my age and up. Apparently, Stefan did not have enough staff to check school attendance. But some of us, the studious kind, diligently marched off to learn. Unfortunately, this "march" to school turned into a path of endurance, because regardless of whether we walked or rode the streetcar, we were subjected to the whistles and taunts of Polish hooligans.

One particular morning, I was caught from behind by two boys and a girl who pulled my braids so hard that I screamed. Fighting like a demon, I managed to free myself and jump onto the streetcar. But my hopes of losing the hoodlums were dashed when I saw them jump aboard after me. They locked me in an embrace and snatched my bookbag. I was terrified that they might throw it out of the window, which would be awful because these books in it had been sent from Palestine, and were irreplaceable. So far, they kept tossing my bag from one to the other, chanting their idiot song. "Die, dirty Jewish brat!"

At that moment I noticed an older lady in a babushka who reminded me of Petrovna. I moved close to her and pleaded, "Please, madam, would you help me get my bookbag from them?"

She looked at me, amused. "Why are you so afraid, child? They don't mean any harm. They are playing games. Boys will be boys. These are good Christian children."

Thank God, the monsters got tired of the game, threw my

bag on the floor, and jumped off the streetcar.

I met my mother every Sunday in the park, and she bought me an Eskimo Pie. One Sunday, she wore a strange-looking hat, grey felt in the shape of a cone. She saw me staring. "I found it in the last shipment from the Joint Distribution Committee in America," she explained. "I was told that Jews there collect used clothing and ship them to us. Your grandmother Jadwiga would have died of shame."

"It's a very pretty hat."

"It's a warm hat." Mother's voice sounded apologetic. But she was right; if a ridiculous hat kept you warm, so be it.

Unlike in our part of Lodz, the snow in the park was mostly clean. If ours were normal conversations, I would have told Mother that I missed my beaver coat, but any mention of the old days made her weep. Moreover, I could not complain that my stomach hurt more and more, especially now, when I was trying to talk to her, and remembered all the things I was supposed to forget.

Poles were getting ready for Christmas, with a decorated spruce here and there, and those creches with baby Jesus, and all the ancient Jews around him.

Mother smiled. "Next week, January 3, will be your twelfth birthday, and on February 11th, will be Wowka's twenty-second. I wonder what he's doing. I wish I could give presents to both of you. Maybe we can have a large celebration in Palestine."

I changed the subject. "How is everything at the shelter?"

"There's nothing to tell. I sew my shirts and eat my meals."

I didn't think she ate much, because her face looked gaunt,

with sunken eyes and a bloodless complexion.

"Here, Mama," I said, "I brought you a Hebrew book. It's poems by Haim Nahman Bialik, the greatest Hebrew poet of our generation."

She leafed through it and smiled. "You are so smart, you'll learn Hebrew before I do. Wowka also learns languages in no time."

Another subject I must remember to avoid: Wowka. I couldn't bear to think of him anymore. And I could not remember the last time we mentioned Father.

Back at the orphanage, I asked the visiting nurse to give me some more of the white powder she gave me weeks earlier, for my stomach. It helped a little, but the pains continued. Maybe they would never stop.

It was Saturday. On Sunday, I would meet Mother and listen again about her longing for Wowka. I must therefore do something today. I asked Stefan for extra streetcar money, and he gave it to me not asking why. After breakfast I bundled up in boots and mittens, and took the streetcar to the Film Institute. Since it was early in the day, students, all male, were rushing to classes. I approached one. "I am Rala Rubinow, Wlodek's sister. Could you tell him to come out?"

He was a redhead with green eyes, nice colors for a snowy day. "Wlodek Rubinow's sister? He told us he has no family."

"Believe me, he has a sister. And a mother. He used to have a grandfather who was a famous rabbi.'"

The student smiled and shook my hand, "Nice to meet you, Rala."

Soon Wowka came out and walked fast toward the gate where I stood. "What are you doing here, Ralka?"

"I am here to tell you that Mother is in a very bad condition. She is on the brink of collapsing from nerves. She can't sleep, eats little, and is very thin. All she talks about is how much she wants to see you."

"You just had a birthday, Ralka, if I remember correctly. So how old are you?"

"I am ten years younger than you. I am a child."

"No Ralka, you are not a child. You were never a child. You have a character of steel, and that's why I don't need to worry about you. And I'll tell you more. You are here not because you love Mother, but because of some misguided Jewish sense of duty. I am the only one who truly loves Mother."

"So will you come and visit her?"

Wowka looked around at the students rushing by. "If anyone sees me visiting a Jewish institution, my standing here as a genuine Pole and probably my career, will be forever ruined."

I grinned. "Well, good luck with all that Count Rubinow."

The next day, a Sunday, I met my mother in the park, and she bought me an Eskimo pie

CHAPTER FORTY-TWO

Lucy was more like a mother to me than a friend. She warned me every day about possible dangers.

"Remember, when you walk on the street, look down so you don't attract attention," she'd say. She also made sure I ate my string beans and drank my milk."

The good news was that I had a boyfriend by the name of Motti, who was a year older. He was smart enough to appropriate a navy blazer from an American shipment, and also a shirt and tie. The blazer had a green emblem on its pocket, with a hockey stick and the letters T.O. embroidered on it. His eyeglasses made him look noble.

I said to him, "Motti, next time a shipment comes, you must help me find pretty clothes. I can't fight the older girls who grab everything nice." He promised.

Every morning, Motti and I went together to school, often joining several others from the orphanage. But one morning, we found ourselves alone on the road. Not surprisingly, we were attacked by three criminal idiots, older and stronger than us. A scene we had become painfully accustomed to was repeated like a dance, a mazurka, perhaps. They caught up with us, grabbed us by our clothes, kicked us in the legs, punched us in the stomachs, threw our books and notebooks into the snow, stood for a while laughing and picking their noses, spat on us—and left.

I have always had a talent for remembering faces, even of people I had met for a short time. But at this point, perhaps starting with Aloyosha beating me up in Siberia, I could not remember any of the attacking faces. They were indistinguishable, a blob of sordid humanity.

After this last "blob" moved away, Motti and I ached. Still, we collected our things and pushed on to school.

"You know, Rala," he said, "I think that these gangs operate on a schedule, like they have an itinerary to attack Jewish children no matter what school they attend."

"What do we do?"

"I have an idea."

Motti's idea was to tell Heniek, because Heniek was legendary. He was the oldest, eighteen, but lived with us, though sometimes he joined the older people on their trips to Germany. He had been a ghetto fighter at thirteen, then made his way through the sewers to the Aryan side. He was stocky and looked like a Polish peasant. Like Stefan, he had joined the Polish underground, and barely escaped the massacre by the Germans in August, 1944.

Motti, holding an icepack to his face, brought Heniek to look at pathetic me, also with an ice pack. Heniek sat down with us at the kitchen table. "Spectacular," he said, admiring the hooligans' work. "Someone must pay. So, here's my plan: Tomorrow morning, you and the other kids go to school as usual, and leave the rest to

Uncle Heniek."

The next morning our cat and mouse game started. But that day—nothing. Heniek shrugged. "You appear unhappy for not having been attacked."

This "disappointment" happened a few more times, and then, as we had expected—hooligans! We were four kids: Motti and I, plus Aliza and Bronia. We hoped that Heniek, unseen, was close by. These misfits had shown up not on our way to the streetcar, but as we got off on a busy street with passersby. What made this day different from any other was the fact that this gang, the debris of human life, had learned new tricks. No more lashing out and grabbing school bags. Instead, they closed us off in a circle, dancing around and chanting, "Oh Jew, dirty Jew, why didn't Hitler kill all of you!"

Passersby smiled, evidently finding the spectacle amusing. Where was Heniek?

Then we saw his work: blood streaming from two interlocking hands. Their blood, not ours! They screamed like the pigs they were. And there stood Heniek, putting his switchblade back in his pocket. He called to them in a loud voice, "From now on, I am taking these children to school. Spread the word that what happened today, will be much worse in the future."

They fled, and we jumped and rejoiced for our deliverance.

"Will you really come with us to school?" Bronia asked.

"We shall see what we shall see, Bronia. But from now on, you must never be afraid."

One afternoon, Commander Stefan brought in a photographer

and ordered us to put on our best clothes for a group picture. We did just that, appearing in clean clothes, hair brushed and braided in ribbons, and shiny smiles. The photographer snapped the group several times, then took a separate photo of every child. We were delighted when a week later he handed us our photos. I thought I looked very nice. I wondered what Mother would say when we met on Sunday. That day, I put on a new navy wool dress that Motti had managed to wrestle for me from the last shipments of American hand-me-downs.

It was very cold, but Mother announced triumphantly, "Today I shall also eat an Eskimo pie." I laughed, and we enjoyed ourselves more than ever. I showed her my picture, and she asked to keep it. I had promised it to Motti, but I could not disappoint Mother.

It was getting abominably cold. The month of March was in full swing. One day, Commander Stefan called me into his office. "Rala, I'm afraid we were not honest with you children about the photographs. The photographer was paid by an American Jewish organization to send pictures of Jewish orphans to see if families wanted to adopt them."

"So why didn't you tell us?"

He shrugged. "I didn't think it was serious. People don't adopt children from a photograph. But in your case, they did. A rich family in New Orleans wants to adopt you."

I laughed. "This is a joke," I said. "You know I have parents, so why did you send my picture?"

"I am deeply sorry. We sent them all, without thinking."

"Just curious. Where is New Orleans?"

"Somewhere between New York and Florida."

I didn't understand. "New York is in the north, and Florida is in the south. Anyway, I only knew three cities in America. New York, because my uncle Marek used to write stories for a Yiddish newspaper called The Forward, Chicago, where most Jews are employed as gangsters, and Los Angeles, where Jews make films about Christmas."

"That's enough knowledge about America for a girl who will live in Palestine," he said.

The following Sunday I asked Mother. "Have you ever heard of an American city called New Orleans?"

"I once heard that it's a city where they eat all the unkosher fish that we call slime."

"Well, a rich Jewish couple over there wants to adopt me because they saw the picture I gave you."

Mother broke down in tears.   "You should go! It is very nice to be rich. I miss it very much. And there is nothing I can offer you."

"Mama, it's a joke! I didn't think you would take this seriously. I love you, and I will never leave you, I swear to God!" I wiped her tears as we hugged and kissed. Oh, God, I thought. The list of subjects I was not supposed to mention to Mother was growing.

April melted the filthy snow on Wolczanska Street and revealed chipped cobblestones underneath. We dispensed with mittens and hats, wearing sweaters instead of coats. Preparations for Passover were under way. We girls looked splendid in white blouses, a holiday gift from our Party in Palestine. Even the boys looked better than usual. I remember Father's saying that when he was a kid his mother dressed him, and after he got married, his wife did. I promised myself that I would never marry a man who was not capable of dressing himself.

Approaching Passover, it was important to list the things that Socialist Zionists had no problem with: chicken soup and matzoh balls, roasted chicken, fried cutlets, farfel kugel—and all other delicious food. Now, I'll review the stuff that we had problems with: The Ten Plagues; the Exodus from Egypt, the Burning Bush... That is, all the stuff that we could not eat.

Helpfully, we used the Socialist Zionist Haggadah. Commander Stefan read from it. "Passover is the story of bricklayers and carpenters who suffered under the yoke of their Egyptian oppressors, anti Semites who did not allow for the creation of labor unions. Evil tyrannical regimes, be they in Egypt or England, must be punished by the masses. It is important for the proletariat to never be duped by corrupt priests and rabbis who tell them that their misery comes from God."

The meal, cooked by the Christian couple the orphanage employed, was excellent. It was my first Passover seder after we had been separated from my grandfather, Rabbi Jacob Meyer. Some of my tears landed into my tasty chicken soup. I posed myself a question: Grandfather's seder was all about God—no, I am not ignoring the matzoh balls—but without God, there would be no seder, and no Passover, in fact no nothing. Something must be done, but what?

Our Hebrew school gave us a week off for Passover, enough time to pursue the Almighty. I knew there was a synagogue nearby, because every morning on our way to the streetcar, we heard Hebrew chants coming through the window of a building such as ours.

On the first free day after the seder, I went out, dressed in the same festive outfit I had worn the night before. I walked until I heard the chants. They were coming from the building's second floor, where I could make out figures swaying back and forth. I opened the door and found myself in a hallway, rickety wooden steps leading upstairs. I went up, my leather shoes making a creaking noise. Four or five men stared at me as I emerged onto the landing, the kind of men who might have lived on Grandfather's street when Bialystok was still standing.

The men staring at me wore long black robes, shiny and belted, huge prayer shawls draped around their shoulders. Grandfather had one of those, and so did my father and Wowka. But I had never seen their kind of hat: a black round circle, covered with fur. These men must have never shaved their beards or side curls, because they were as long as my braids.

"Who are you, girl?" one of them asked in Yiddish. I heard fervent singing from the other room and noticed their shaking and trembling. "Who are you?" he repeated.

"I am from the orphanage, and I came to say a prayer because it's Passover."

"Do you have a ticket? The staring men asked.

"No, I don't have any money. I'm from the orphanage."

More sternly, one of them asked, "Which orphanage?"

"The Socialist Zionist down the street."

"You can't be here, the Socialist Zionists don't believe in God."

A nicer man chimed in: "Let her in anyway, she's just a kid."

"But she cannot go in dressed like this."

This I did not understand. "Dressed like what?" I asked.

"Child, don't you know that you are almost naked, which for

a young Jewish girl is a terrible sin? You are wearing a short sleeve blouse, and you didn't button your top button. Your skirt is so short it shows your knees, and your legs are bare. We cannot let you join our wives and daughters, because they will be shocked by your appearance."

"My grandfather was a great rabbi," I raised my voice for the first time, "and he would never send away someone who came to pray." I thought they were moving toward me menacingly, but maybe I was wrong. Still, I took a few steps back. Holding onto the banister, I shouted in my best Bialystok Yiddish, "You will all fry in hell!"

Then I turned around and ran.

CHAPTER FORTY-THREE

May 15 was a day of explosive news. The Jews of Palestine declared themselves a state called Israel. Two dozen of us from the orphanage, including Heniek, went to the theatre to see the newsreel. And here it was: a whole segment about creating a brand new country. We sat in the dark, spellbound, watching a man with a mass of unruly white hair speak from a podium to a mesmerized crowd, behind him blue-and-white flags with a Star of David in the middle. His name was David Ben-Gurion, and he was reading a document called "The Declaration of Independence." We all rose and applauded. We applauded so hard that nothing else could be heard in the auditorium.

Then we left, not bothering to find out what movie was playing.

At breakfast, Commander Stefan explained that from now on, we were citizens of Israel. Every Jew in the world was a citizen of Israel. This was due to what was called "The Law of Return." We were so shocked that we ate our breakfast in near-silence.

On Sunday, as always, I met Mother in the park. We sat on what we had dubbed our bench. The sun was shining amiably, and a breeze cooled our faces. I wanted to discuss with Mother how the State of Israel might change our lives. But she seemed to enjoy the sun and peace so much that I decided not to discuss anything. I would need to answer my own questions.

But she was thinking along similar lines, apparently. "Rala, it's great that your aunts are now living in their own country."

This gave me an opening. "Mama, did you finally tell Zila and Mina the truth?"

"Absolutely not! In our family, I was considered the richest and most successful. Did you know that I heard in Bialystok that the Rakowskis had a lot of jewelry to sell? I am proud of having been rich enough to provide it." Mother burst in tears.

"Yes, Mama." She should not have mentioned the jewelry. She cried for longer than usual. When I finally managed to put her on the streetcar, I realized that I had missed Eskimo Pie.

I must do something about our situation. I remembered Zila's address from years of correspondence: 9 Balfour Street, Haifa, Palestine. No! Haifa, Israel! I tore a page out of a notebook and wrote, "Dear Aunts Zila and Mina and Uncle David and also Great Aunt Puah who is among the Founders! Congratulations on living in a country! I am writing to tell you the truth: Everything Mother wrote to you in the last two years IS A LIE. She is ashamed to admit that two years ago Father abandoned us and escaped to Vienna, on some pretext that he was smuggling Jews across a border. Mother has been living in a shelter for homeless Jewish refugees, and I live in an orphanage.

"Actually, I am doing fine, but Mother is not. She is in very bad shape. She eats very little, and she is skin and bones. Her work in the shelter is sewing shirts, and she hates it. I think if you don't get us out of here, Mother will die.

"I swear to God that I am not exaggerating. I thank you for everything you have done for us when we were in Siberia. What we need now is to put us on a priority list for shipment to Israel. With great love, I am, Rala."

News from Israel was grim. All the Arab states attacked us with huge armies, which shows that not only Poles are anti-Semites, but also Arabs. Because of the war, Commander Stefan gave us small tin boxes to go out and collect money to plant trees in Israel. I heard that parts of Israel were desert, so planting trees was a good idea. With the box, I received two addresses. Stefan said, "The addresses are of shops owned by Jews, so there will not be a problem."

The next afternoon, a car dropped us off at the Lodz business center. "Everyone please return here in one hour," the driver said, "and then we'll go for ice cream."

We dispersed to find our addresses. I found my first address easily, but there was a problem. Before me was not one shop, but two. I looked into their windows. No customers in either store. On the left was an old man sitting alone on a stool. Impossible to guess what business he was in. In the right window was a couple arranging rolls of fabrics on shelves. Everyone in Bialystok worked in textiles, a singularly Jewish business.

I knocked on the door of the fabric store and stepped in. "Good afternoon," I said in my most dignified manner. I extended my box with the blue Star of David and asked for a donation to the

Jewish National Fund to plant trees in Israel.

The woman shrieked, "Ahhhh!" and stood petrified staring at me, clutching a roll of black-and-white tweed. Again, but louder, "Ahhhh!"

Could it be that I was in the wrong shops, and these people were not Jews? Even so, the woman's behavior was not from this world, but from a scary story. Curiously, I observed her staring at me as if I was a black cat. She cried some more, and gasped. Her husband took the fabric out of her arms, and hugged her. I stood there, as if watching a movie and waiting for the rest of the plot. The woman tore herself away from her husband, lifted the counter that separated us, and advanced towards me.

The man shouted, "Please child, leave immediately!"

I sprinted out of the store as fast as I could. Exhaling, I tried to calm myself. Then I noticed a garbage can and tossed collection-box inside. The old man in the other store used a hammer on a shoe sole. Ah, a cobbler, also a Jewish profession. I smiled and waved to him.

The ice cream afterwards was great!

A day later in school, Mr. Most, the principal, called me to his office, and there was Mr. Itzik Kantor. He looked as harassed as ever, still unshaven, wearing a green vest, a ridiculous garment for a one-armed man.

"Good news, Rala. I have orders from the Jewish Agency in Jerusalem to put you and your mother on the next transport from Lodz. It'll be Thursday, five days from now."

I gulped. Then I jumped up and kissed him.

"Why didn't your mother tell me that Puah Rakowski is her aunt?"

"Because, Mr. Itzik, we didn't know how the system works. But I'm learning."

He coughed, which I interpreted as embarrassment. "Anyway, I thought I would tell you first, not wanting to surprise your mother."

Mr. Most took me back to class. I stood in front of everyone and announced, "On Thursday my mother and I are leaving for Israel."

Everyone cheered and ran up to hug me. This was not an unusual announcement, however. Every few days, someone else arrived with the same good news. A sense of impermanence reigned in the school and the orphanage, as we, the last Jews in Poland, were packing up, never to return.

I collected my books and walked with Itzik downstairs, where he put me next to him in a dusty black car. He was the driver. Yuk! Wouldn't it be funny if after everything that happened, I would die driven by a man who only had a left arm, and before he had lost it, he was right-handed?

We started counting the days. Mother said that she had sent a message to Wowka through Mr. Itzik, to come to the park and say good-bye. So here he was, my brother Wowka. But he was not alone. With him was a tall, very pretty girl. Both of them were beautifully dressed, Wowka in a suit and tie and very adult-looking grey fedora, the girl in a white suit and a pink hat with a white feather.

"Mama, Ralka, please meet my wife Irena Krawczynska, Isia for short."

Mother looked at Irena with such astonishment that her eyes failed to blink even once. I was so stunned that I dropped my Eskimo pie.

Irena was first to speak. "My uncle Tadeusz was a prisoner in Auschwitz..." She continued talking about her family, but we weren't listening.

Wowka cut her short. "Mama, Ralka, Isia and I are invited for cocktails at Elsa's. Must run."

Mother said, "Rala and I are leaving for Israel on Thursday."

The two of them kissed us. "I hope you enjoy Puah's Zionist dream," my brother said, and took off with his wife.

"Oh, Rala, I'll never see him again."

"Who knows? Somehow he always turns up."

Thursday morning, Mother and I waited for Itzik at the shelter. Now that we were his privileged customers, he got rid of our big unwieldy suitcase and replaced it with two medium ones that were more than adequate for our possessions. Thus was gone the fine leather suitcase of us aristocrats! He drove us to the railroad station, and handed us an envelope with money.

"Francs. You can use them in Marseilles until the ship arrives." Mother put the money into her brasserie. Maybe in Israel she would once more carry money in a handbag.

"This train will take you to Warsaw, where you will transfer to one headed for Vienna, Paris and Marseilles. And then—Haifa! A gift." He opened his rucksack and handed us each a tin of American peanuts and a chunky chocolate bar.

"I've never tasted peanuts," I said. "It will be interesting."

Itzik was almost gone, but then he turned around. "Mrs.

Rubinow. I am sorry for everything that happened to you and Rachel. I feel that there was a great deal of misunderstanding. I am thrilled that your family intervened."

Itzik Kantor was the last Jew we saw in Poland.

CHAPTER FORTY-FOUR

The Warsaw train chugged along toward our next stop, Prague, the capital of Chekhoslovakia. As we left Poland behind, we opened the first tin of peanuts and munched them slowly, deliberately. Wonderful new taste, salty, crackling.

"Chew slowly," Mother admonished, "nuts are hard to digest."

We hid the chocolate bars in Mother's pocketbook and ate half of a cheese sandwich we had bought at the Warsaw railroad station. There was a faucet on the train and we drank from it.

Then it was Prague. We rolled down the car windows and viewed the platform, surprised to see friendly, smiling people. I listened carefully to their voices, able to distinguish familiar words because Czech is a Slavic language like Polish. It turned out that many of the people milling around were not travelers, but traders. Czechoslovakia remained an important manufacturing center, so people traded jewelry, crystal goblets, embroidered shawls, and a lot else. What they had little of was food. They were looking to barter their craftsmanship for something to eat.

I noticed an older boy, holding up a pen. I stretched my arm out of the window and asked in slow Polish, "May I hold it?"

He let me. It was a magic pen with four colors: red, green, blue and black. Four buttons allowed you to get whichever color you wanted. I pressed—and out popped red, pressed again—now it was green. I could write an essay in four colors!

I offered him my chocolate bar for the pen, and he nodded eagerly. Since Mother was dozing, I retrieved my chocolate and handed it to the boy. He was happy, and I had just concluded the first important trade of my life. I reached for one of my notebooks and doodled hearts and angels in four different colors.

The next morning, we crossed into Austria.

Mother said, "Itzik told me that he contacted Kuba about our train schedule. He sent back a message that he would get on in Salzburg and ride with us for a couple of hours." Mother's face showed anxiety, even fear. I had no reason to love my father anymore. Still, I had no idea how I would feel when I saw him.

"Salzburg!"

And there was Father, on the platform running toward the train. He jumped in, kissed Mother, kissed me and lifted me in the air. "You are not as tiny as you used to be, Ralichka."

We sat down in our compartment, Mother and I on one side, Father across. He looked elegant in a Tyrolean green jacket, a jaunty haircut and attractive black-rimmed glasses. Very handsome was my father. He was also checking us out. I hoped Mother did not detect the wince in his eyes as he observed her. I gave him what I considered to be a ruthless stare, and he lowered his eyes. Did he want us back? Did we?

"Ralichka, you look pretty and grown up." Please, Papa, I

thought. Say something nice to your wife. He brought us presents, a mountain jacket for Mother and another one for me.

"I don't really need it," I said. "I think it'll be too warm for Israel."

But Mother said, "Thank you."

He extended an envelope toward her. "Dollars, the best currency in the world."

She looked at the outstretched envelope, not reaching for it. I sucked in my breath. If she refuses, it's the end. But Mother stretched out her arm and put the envelope in her handbag. Neither of us offered thanks.

"Papa," I asked. "Why didn't you bring us to live with you?"

He looked perplexed. Mother smiled; she knew I was doing it for her.

"I have a small apartment and it's not enough for three people."

I persisted.: "So why didn't you turn heaven and earth to get us passage to Israel?"

His eyes tightened. "It's for your own good. There's a war going on between Jews and Arabs, and Jews are killed every day. It would have been safer for you to wait till the war was over. But you, Fira, couldn't wait. So you brought the great Puah into it."

"Mama had nothing to do with this. I was the one who wrote the letter to Zila, Mina and Puah."

Father shook his head. "First, your brother disobeys me, and now you follow in his footsteps. No matter. Soon I will join you in Israel. But first I must smuggle several transports of refugees across the border."

The conductor shouted the name of a station.

"My stop." Father kissed Mother on both cheeks.

I stood in his way and said, "Father, kiss me."

He looked at me. "I kissed you when I got on the train."

Then he jumped off.

Next, we arrived in Paris. In the movies, wonderful adventures await people who visit Paris. In this city, my grandmother Jadwiga had taught herself to be a designer. It was also the city where Father had bought for me wonderful dolls.

"You know, Mama," I said at one point. "This is the first time we are in a country where we cannot speak the language."

But somehow, with motions and smiles, we were helped by strangers to locate the track for Marseille. We sat on a bench waiting for our train. The throng around us paid us no attention. Ah, great! From a vendor, we bought sausages inside a bun and a bottle of orange soda. I bit into my sandwich, and it was the greatest meat I had ever eaten. What a trip! I discovered peanuts, bartered for a magical pen, ate French sausage in a bun, drank orange soda, and was sure that Mother would give me a piece of her chocolate bar.

My life was definitely improving.

CHAPTER FORTY-FIVE

We had enough francs for a taxi. Our destination was Port de Marseille DP Camp. Hearing the address, the driver demanded payment up front.

This camp had no barbed wire, but an ordinary wooden fence with a gate and a Yiddish- speaking guard. He phoned someone about our arrival, and soon a young man drove up in an American car and took us inside, in the direction of half a dozen barracks built with little land between them.

I asked the driver, "Was this built for the French Legion? I read a book about them."

The driver didn't answer, so maybe he didn't speak Yiddish. He led us to a dormitory as large as the one in Old Mud, but nicer. The mattresses were mostly clean and covered with sheets, and the pillows had pillowcases. We had but one blanket apiece, but it was enough on this warm Mediterranean seacoast. We found two cots together in the middle of a long row, made our beds for sleep, and stashed our suitcases underneath.

"Rala, we have enough francs to find a nice café overlooking the water and have a café filtre and a napoleon."

Another new addition to my life would be coffee and famous French pastry. I knew who Napoleon Bonaparte was, but I had no idea that he was also a baker. We proceeded towards the beachfront, passing shops advertising "tabac" and "pernod." Shady- looking men in berets strolled on the promenade. Mother laughed. "These characters look like they came directly from Pepe Le Moko."

"Huh?"

"He's someone I saw in a French film before the war, with the French actor Jean Gabin. Pepe was a criminal in love with a beautiful girl. Legend has it that Frenchmen are great lovers. Maybe someday you'll find out."

"Mother!" I blushed.

We picked an elegant coffee shop and sat by the window overlooking a serene blue sea. Mother ordered in what suddenly appeared to be a cultivated new voice. I dug into the pastry for which Mother had longed for so many years. It tasted like very nice pudding layered in between crunchy pastry leaves. I took a sip of coffee. Bitter and hot, it made my head spin. But this was sophistication. I was determined to learn to like it.

Mother chewed with her eyes closed, sucking the pudding between the leaves. For her, obviously, the napoleon was more than cake.

Back in the camp, we learned that our ship would sail in three days. Mother stared at me with unusual concentration. "We must make you look prettier when we get off the boat in Haifa."

"Mother, you always said I was pretty."

"A pretty girl must always try to look prettier."

From under the bed, Mother pulled out a coal iron and a wand, which looked like a medieval torture instrument. She continued, "When we arrive in Israel I want you to look like Shirleyka. Your aunts and Puah will be very impressed."

"But why are you firing up a coal iron in the dormitory? I'm sure it's against the law. And who is this Shirleyka I'm supposed to look like?"

"She is a child actress in American movies. Her name is Shirley Temple, but in Poland we call her Shirleyka."

"How old is she?"

Mother did not answer immediately. "Well, I'm thinking. Maybe seven."

"Mama, in a few weeks I'll be thirteen. I don't want to look seven."

Mother burst into tears. "Are you angry with me? Please, you must never be angry with me."

Of course I let her mutilate my hair with a hot wand. I felt hot and steamy. "Enough, Mama, please!"

"You do look like Shirleyka, very becoming!"

She finally let me be. I looked around the dormitory to see who had a mirror on the wall. There, in the right corner. I took a look at myself. Horror! If Mother were not so prone to tears, I would have sobbed my heart out in front of everyone.

The ship's name was Negba, meaning in Hebrew southbound. She was an unkempt Greek boat leased by the Zionists to carry refugees to Israel. The original name Acropolis was only partially wiped off. It was definitely not a passenger ship, just as the echelons had not been passenger trains.

There were no beds, no bunks, nothing. This ship could not possibly carry eight-hundred humans across this Mediterranean. We shall see! Everyone pushed to find a spot on the two decks. Mother and I emerged on the upper deck, and sat on a pile of ropes. There were at least thirty others stretched along the same pile.

The journey should take four days, people said. The first day was pleasant, if you ignored the ropes digging into your flesh. The stars above flickered playfully, and the water was a cascade of pristine blue. Cooking was impossible, so we ate cold food, such as cans of sardines, bread, apples, hard-boiled eggs and once or twice a tomato.

The second day was a repeat of the first. Breakfast was black bread with strawberry jam, milk for kids, water for adults. Shirley Temple thirstily drank her milk, but her curls had gotten sticky and disgusting from the sea air.

On the third day the sea turned wavy, and the ship was tossed as if by an absent-minded sea creature. On our upper deck, we welcomed a guest. His name was Dr. Zvi Bar-Shalom, a literature professor at the Hebrew University in Jerusalem. He used a bullhorn, so he could be heard over the roaring waves.

Dr. Zvi said, "I am going to tell you a story written by Yehuda Leib Peretz, the greatest Yiddish writer who ever lived. The name of the story is 'The Elk.' So, once upon a time in a shtetl in Poland, lived a beautiful elk with the tallest horns in the entire county. When a pogrom appeared in the village, the elk would reach up to Heaven with his horns, asking God to have mercy. And every time, the hooligans would be wracked with pain and run away. This happened many times a year, until the hooligans got scared and put an end to the pogroms. The village residents relaxed, basking in peace and prosperity.

"After a while, a fancy Jewish merchant called Goldshmitt saw the elk prancing gracefully in the forest, and said to himself: If I cut just a little bit of the horn, I can make myself a beautiful snuffbox. Soon his snuffbox became the envy of every man in the village.

"The villagers believed that they were as special as the fancy merchant and were also entitled to a snuff box. Each day, one or two would venture into the meadow for pieces of the elk's horns to shape them into snuff boxes. Soon every man in town had a snuffbox and bragged that his was the best.

"As time went by, the Poles started longing for pogroms. So they gathered their forces and attacked the Jews with shovels and pitchforks. The Jews ran into the meadow to beg the elk to intercede with God. But something awful had happened: the elk's horns were too short to reach the Almighty's ears."

There was a moral to the story, but the wind intensified and drowned it out.

The fourth day returned to gorgeous. We sailed slowly on luxurious, soothing waves.

Suddenly on the horizon we saw the contours of the Land of Israel. The setting sun mixed blue with orange, and the air felt fresh and pure.

"Rala, do you think God created this beauty?" my mother asked.

"I don't know." Four women waited for us as we disembarked.

Mother shouted, "Zila, Mina!"

She and her sisters choked each other with kisses and embraces. I also fell into their arms. Everyone wept.

But there was another woman standing there, whose eyes remained dry. She was the oldest human being I had ever seen. Her face and neck were a mass of wrinkles and folds, as must be her thin body under an elegant silk dress. She was far different than what I imagined a pioneer and Founder to look. She also wore a perky straw hat with a navy ribbon.

I stared at Puah Rakowski, one of the greats, and my grandfather's sister.

"Aunt Puah, how are you?" Mother asked. Puah scrutinized us with what I thought was disappointment. I couldn't blame her. Was this the only remnant of the great Rakowski clan? This woman with the hollow eyes, and the child with dirty curls?

Behind Puah was a fourth woman, about my aunts' and Mother's age, who bore a significance resemblance to Puah. She balanced three newspapers in her arms.

"Great-Aunt Puah, why do you need three newspapers?"

She looked at me and smiled. "This is a very intelligent question, Rala. A smart Rakowski question. The answer is: one is from my own party, the other from crazy Bolsheviks, and the third from zealots with sidecurls. Ah, meet my daughter, Sarah Cohen." She pointed to the lady with the newspapers.

Then we stood silently, subdued by the enormity of the occasion.

Great Aunt Puah brought us back to reality. She took my hand and said, "Come Rala. Let's go home."

Doreen Patron
Rachel's daughter, soaks in views of the
Mediterranean Sea from Haifa.

Great Aunt Puah Rakowski
one of Israel's founders, greeted Esther and Rala
upon their arrival in Haifa in January 1949.